OCR GCSE MATHEMATICS

STAGE 7

GRADUATED ASSESSMENT

SECOND EDITION

- Howard Baxter
- Michael Handbury
- John Jeskins
- Jean Matthews
- Mark Patmore

Hodder Murray

A MEMBER OF THE HODDER HEADLINE GROUP

The Publishers would like to thank the following for permission to reproduce copyright material:

Photo credits
p.18 © www.purestockX.com; p.118 © AM Corporation/Alamy; p.119 (left)
© Turbo/zefa/Corbis, (right) © Dennis Hallinan/Alamy; p.120 © David L. Moore/Alamy;
p.145 © Jutta Klee/Corbis.

Hodder Headline's policy is to use papers that are natural, renewable and recyclable products
and made from wood grown in sustainable forests. The logging and manufacturing processes
are expected to conform to the environmental regulations of the country of origin.

Orders: please contact Bookpoint Ltd, 130 Milton Park, Abingdon, Oxon OX14 4SB.
Telephone: (44) 01235 827720. Fax: (44) 01235 400454. Lines are open from 9 a.m. to 5 p.m.,
Monday to Saturday, with a 24-hour message-answering service. Visit our website at
www.hoddereducation.co.uk.

© Howard Baxter, Michael Handbury, John Jeskins, Jean Matthews, Mark Patmore,
Brian Seager, Eddie Wilde, 2006
First published in 2006 by
Hodder Murray, an imprint of Hodder Education,
a member of the Hodder Headline Group,
338 Euston Road,
London NW1 3BH

Impression number   10 9 8 7 6 5 4 3 2 1
Year   2011 2010 2009 2008 2007 2006

Cover photo © Andy Sacks/Photographer's Choice/Getty Images
Illustrations © Barking Dog
Typeset in 10/12 TimesTen by Pantek Arts Ltd, Maidstone, Kent
Printed in Great Britain by CPI Bath.

A catalogue record for this title is available from the British Library

ISBN-10: 0340 915 943
ISBN-13: 978 0340 915 943

Contents

STAGE
7

STAGE
7

Contents

STAGE
7

Introduction

About this book

This course has been written especially for students following OCR's 2006 Modular Specification C, Graduated Assessment (J516) for GCSE Mathematics.

This book covers the complete specification for Stage 7.

- Each chapter is presented in a way which will help you to understand the mathematics, with straightforward explanations and worked examples covering every type of problem.
- At the start of each chapter are two lists, one of what you should already know before you begin and the other of the topics you will be learning about in that chapter.
- 'Activities' offer a more interesting approach to the core content, giving opportunities for you to develop your skills.
- 'Challenges' are rather more searching and are designed to make you think mathematically.
- There are plenty of exercises to work through to practise your skills.
- Some questions are designed to be done without a calculator, so that you can practise for the non-calculator sections of the examination papers.
- Look out for the 'Exam tips' – these give advice on how to improve your performance in the module test, direct from the experienced examiners who have written this book.
- At the end of each chapter there is a short summary of what you have learned.
- Finally, there are 'Revision exercises' at intervals throughout the book to help you revise all the topics covered in the preceding chapters.

Other components in the series

- A Homework Book
  This contains parallel exercises to those in this book to give you more practice. Included with the Homework Book is a Personal Tutor CD-ROM. This will help you if you have to miss a lesson or if you need a reminder of something taught in class.

STAGE
7

- An Assessment Pack

  There are two Assessment Packs: one for Foundation Tier (Stages 1 to 7) and one for Higher Tier (Stages 6 to 10). Each contains revision exercises, practice module papers and a practice terminal paper to help you prepare for the examination. Some of the questions in the examination will offer you little help to get started. These are called 'unstructured' or 'multi-step' questions. Instead of the question having several parts, each of which helps you to answer the next, you have to work out the necessary steps to find the answer. There will be examples of this kind of question in the Assessment Pack.

- An Interactive Investigations CD-ROM

  This contains whole-class presentations and individual activities. It helps you understand how you can best use ICT to do your homework and other tasks.

Top ten tips

Here are some general tips from the examiners who wrote this book to help you to do well in your tests and examinations.

Practise

1 **taking time** to work through each question carefully.
2 answering questions **without** a calculator.
3 answering questions which require **explanations**.
4 answering **unstructured** questions.
5 **accurate** drawing and construction.
6 answering questions which **need a calculator**, trying to use it efficiently.
7 **checking answers**, especially for reasonable size and degree of accuracy.
8 making your work **concise** and well laid out.
9 checking that you have **answered the question**.
10 **rounding** numbers, but only at the appropriate stage.

Coordinates

You will learn about

- Finding the coordinates of the midpoint of a line
- Using coordinates in three dimensions (3-D)

You should already know

- How to use coordinates in two dimensions

Midpoints

ACTIVITY 1

For each of these pairs of points:

- Draw a diagram on squared paper. The first one is done for you.
- Find the middle point of the line joining the two points.
- Label this point M.
- Write down the coordinates of M.

a) A(1, 3) and B(5, 7)
b) C(1, 5) and D(7, 1)
c) E(2, 5) and F(6, 6)
d) G(3, 7) and H(6, 0)

What do you notice?

EXAM TIP
'Middle point' is often shortened to **midpoint**.

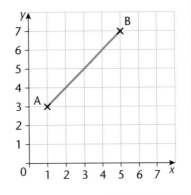

STAGE 7

The coordinates of the midpoint of a line between two points are the mean of the coordinates of the two points.

Midpoint of line between points with coordinates (a, b) and $(c, d) = \left(\dfrac{a + c}{2}, \dfrac{b + d}{2}\right)$.

▌▌▌ EXAMPLE 1

Find the coordinates of the midpoint of the line joining each of these pairs of points without drawing the graph.

a) A(2, 1) and B(6, 7)

b) C(‑2, 1) and D(2, 5)

a) A(2, 1) and B(6, 7)
$a = 2, b = 1, c = 6, d = 7$

$$\text{Midpoint} = \left(\frac{a + c}{2}, \frac{b + d}{2}\right)$$

$$= \left(\frac{2 + 6}{2}, \frac{1 + 7}{2}\right)$$

$$= (4, 4)$$

b) C(‑2, 1) and D(2, 5)
$a = {}^-2, b = 1, c = 2, d = 5$

$$\text{Midpoint} = \left(\frac{a + c}{2}, \frac{b + d}{2}\right)$$

$$= \left(\frac{{}^-2 + 2}{2}, \frac{1 + 5}{2}\right)$$

$$= (0, 3)$$

You can check your answers by drawing the graph of the line.

EXERCISE 1.1

1 Find the coordinates of the midpoint of each of these lines.

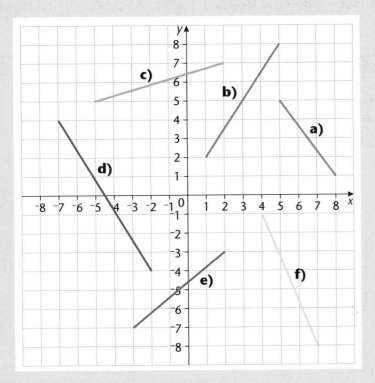

2 Find the coordinates of the midpoint of the line joining each of these pairs of points. Try to do it without plotting the points.
a) A(1, 4) and B(1, 8)
b) C(1, 5) and D(7, 3)
c) E(2, 3) and F(8, 6)
d) G(3, 7) and H(8, 2)
e) I(⁻2, 3) and J(4, 1)
f) K(⁻4, ⁻3) and L(⁻6, ⁻11)

3 Find the coordinates of the midpoint of each side of this shape.

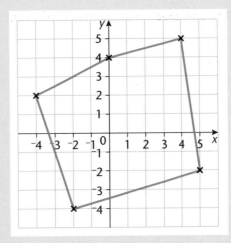

Three-dimensional (3-D) coordinates

You already know how to describe a point using coordinates in two dimensions. You use x- and y-coordinates.

If you are working in three dimensions you need a third coordinate. This is known as the z-coordinate.

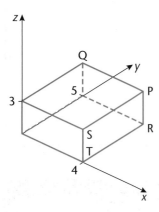

> ### EXAM TIP
> Notice that the x- and y-axes lie flat with the z-axis vertical.

The coordinates of point P are (4, 5, 3).

That is, 4 in the x-direction, 5 in the y-direction and 3 in the z-direction.

> ### EXAM TIP
> As with 2-D coordinates, 3-D coordinates are written in alphabetical order: x then y then z.

 ACTIVITY 2

Write down the coordinates of the points Q, R, S and T in the diagram above.

You know that in two dimensions the coordinates of the midpoint of a line between two points are the mean of the coordinates of the two points.

This is also true in three dimensions.

Midpoint of line between points with coordinates (a, b, c) and $(d, e, f) = \left(\dfrac{a+d}{2}, \dfrac{b+e}{2}, \dfrac{c+f}{2}\right)$.

EXAMPLE 2

A is the point (4, 2, 3) and B is the point (2, 6, 9).

What are the coordinates of the midpoint of AB?

A(4, 2, 3) and B(2, 6, 9)
$a = 4$, $b = 2$, $c = 3$, $d = 2$, $e = 6$, $f = 9$

$$\text{Midpoint} = \left(\frac{a + d}{2}, \frac{b + e}{2}, \frac{c + f}{2} \right)$$

$$= \left(\frac{4 + 2}{2}, \frac{2 + 6}{2}, \frac{3 + 9}{2} \right)$$

$$= (3, 4, 6)$$

EXERCISE 1.2

1 The diagram shows the outline of a cuboid.

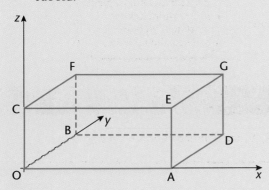

The coordinates of point A are (5, 0, 0).
The coordinates of point B are (0, 3, 0).
The coordinates of point C are (0, 0, 2).

Write down the coordinates of each of these points.
a) D
b) E
c) F
d) G

2 VOABC is a square-based pyramid.

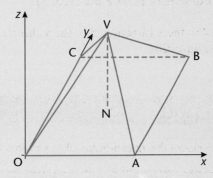

A is the point (6, 0, 0).
N is the centre of the base.
The perpendicular height VN of the pyramid is 5 units.

Write down the coordinates of each of these points.
a) C
b) B
c) N
d) V

STAGE

7

EXERCISE 1.2 continued

3 The diagram shows the outline of a cuboid.

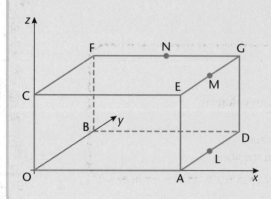

The coordinates of point A are $(8, 0, 0)$.
The coordinates of point B are $(0, 6, 0)$.
The coordinates of point C are $(0, 0, 4)$.

L is the midpoint of AD.
M is the midpoint of EG.
N is the midpoint of FG.

Write down the coordinates of each of these points.
a) D
b) L
c) M
d) N

C CHALLENGE 1

ABCDEFGH is a cuboid.

A is the point $(2, 3, 4)$.

AB is 7 units long and is parallel to the *x*-axis.

AD is 1 unit long and is parallel to the *y*-axis.

AE is 3 units long and is parallel to the *z*-axis.

Find the coordinates of the points
B, C, D, E, F, G and H.

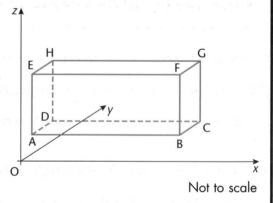

Not to scale

K KEY IDEAS

- The coordinates of the midpoint of the line joining (a, b) to (c, d) are $\left(\dfrac{a + c}{2}, \dfrac{b + d}{2}\right)$.

- In three dimensions a point has three coordinates.
  The third coordinate is the *z*-coordinate.

- The coordinates of the midpoint of the line joining (a, b, c) to (d, e, f)
  are $\left(\dfrac{a + d}{2}, \dfrac{b + e}{2}, \dfrac{c + f}{2}\right)$.

Percentages

You will learn about

- Changing between fractions, decimals and percentages
- Using percentages to compare proportions
- Finding the percentage of an increase or decrease
- Increasing and decreasing a quantity by a percentage

You should already know

- How to write and read fractions, decimals and percentages
- How to multiply and divide numbers and decimals by 100

You should also know that percentage means 'out of 100'. For example

'75% of cat owners surveyed said their cats preferred fish-flavoured treats.'

75% means that 75 out of every 100 people surveyed said their cats preferred fish-flavoured treats.

'40% of people asked said they drank coffee at breakfast.'

40% means that 40 people out of every 100 people drank coffee at breakfast.

ACTIVITY 1

Find as many examples of percentages as you can from newspapers, magazines and advertising material.

STAGE
7

The equivalence of fractions, decimals and percentages

Seven out of 10 households buy their milk at supermarkets.
What is this as a percentage?

You can work this out either by using equivalent fractions

$\frac{7}{10} = \frac{70}{100} = 70\%$ (multiplying the numerator and the denominator by 10)

or by changing the fraction to a decimal

$\frac{7}{10} = 0 \cdot 7 = 70\%$.

To change a fraction into a decimal, remember to divide the numerator by the denominator, as shown in Example 1.

EXAMPLE 1

Convert $\frac{3}{8}$ to   **a)** a decimal.   **b)** a percentage.

a) $\frac{3}{8} = 3 \div 8 = 0 \cdot 375$

b) $0 \cdot 375 \times 100 = 37 \cdot 5\%$
It is possible to go straight from the fraction to the percentage using multiplication of fractions.

$\frac{3}{8} \times 100 = \frac{3}{8} \times \frac{100}{1} = \frac{300}{8} = 37 \cdot 5\%$

A ACTIVITY 2

Use percentages to put each set of numbers in order, smallest first.

a) $0 \cdot 3, \quad \frac{1}{3}, \quad 0 \cdot 33, \quad \frac{4}{9}, \quad \frac{5}{11}, \quad \frac{2}{5}, \quad \frac{2}{7}$

b) $\frac{7}{9}, \quad \frac{2}{3}, \quad 0 \cdot 7, \quad \frac{3}{5}, \quad \frac{8}{11}, \quad 0 \cdot 666$

STAGE
7

EXERCISE 2.1

1 Change each of these percentages to a fraction. Write your answers in their lowest terms.
- **a)** 35%
- **b)** 65%
- **c)** 8%
- **d)** 120%

2 Change each of these percentages to a decimal.
- **a)** 16%
- **b)** 27%
- **c)** 83%
- **d)** 7%
- **e)** 31%
- **f)** 4%
- **g)** 17%
- **h)** 2%
- **i)** 150%
- **j)** 250%
- **k)** 9%
- **l)** 12·5%

3 Change each of these decimals to a percentage.
- **a)** 0·62
- **b)** 0·56
- **c)** 0·04
- **d)** 0·165
- **e)** 1·32
- **f)** 0·37
- **g)** 0·83
- **h)** 0·08
- **i)** 0·345
- **j)** 1·25

4 Copy this table and complete it.

Fraction $\frac{a}{b}$	Decimal $a \div b$	Percentage = decimal $\times$ 100
$\frac{7}{10}$		
$\frac{2}{5}$		
$\frac{3}{4}$		
$\frac{1}{3}$		
$\frac{2}{3}$		

5 Change each of these fractions to a decimal.
- **a)** $\frac{1}{100}$
- **b)** $\frac{17}{100}$
- **c)** $\frac{2}{50}$
- **d)** $\frac{8}{5}$
- **e)** $\frac{1}{8}$
- **f)** $\frac{3}{8}$
- **g)** $\frac{3}{20}$
- **h)** $\frac{17}{40}$
- **i)** $\frac{5}{16}$

6 Change each decimal you found in question **5** to a percentage.

7 Change each of these fractions into a percentage. Give your answers correct to 1 decimal place.
- **a)** $\frac{1}{6}$
- **b)** $\frac{5}{6}$
- **c)** $\frac{5}{12}$
- **d)** $\frac{1}{12}$
- **e)** $\frac{3}{70}$

8 On Wednesday, 0·23 of the population watched EastEnders. What percentage is this?

9 At a matinée, $\frac{4}{5}$ of the audience at the pantomime were children. What percentage is this?

10 In a survey, $\frac{3}{10}$ of children liked cheese and onion crisps. What percentage is this?

11 A kilometre is $\frac{5}{8}$ of a mile. What percentage is this?

12 The winning candidate in an election gained $\frac{7}{12}$ of the votes. What percentage is this? Give your answer correct to the nearest 1%.

13 Nicola spends $\frac{3}{7}$ of her pocket money on sweets and drinks. What percentage is this? Give your answer correct to the nearest 1%.

14 Imran has a part-time job. He saves $\frac{2}{9}$ of his wages. What percentage is this? Give your answer correct to the nearest 1%.

EXAM TIP

For the non-calculator section of the examination papers it is worth learning some basic equivalents.

$\frac{1}{2} = 0.5 = 50\%$ $\frac{1}{3} = 0.333\ldots = 33.3\ldots\%$ $\frac{1}{5} = 0.2 = 20\%$

$\frac{1}{4} = 0.25 = 25\%$ (33% to the nearest 1%) $\frac{2}{5} = 0.4 = 40\%$

$\frac{3}{4} = 0.75 = 75\%$ $\frac{2}{3} = 0.666\ldots = 66.6\ldots\%$ $\frac{3}{5} = 0.6 = 60\%$

                 (67% to the nearest 1%) $\frac{4}{5} = 0.8 = 80\%$

Notice the rounding of $\frac{1}{3}$ and $\frac{2}{3}$. It is a common error to think that $\frac{1}{3} = 0.3 = 30\%$ and $\frac{2}{3} = 0.66 = 66\%$ or even $\frac{2}{3} = 0.6 = 60\%$.

Percentage increases and decreases

In this section you will use methods you have learned previously to solve problems.

Finding the percentage

Percentage increases and decreases are worked out as percentages of the original amount, not the new amount. Percentage profit or loss is worked out as a percentage of the cost price, not the selling price.

EXAMPLE 2

An art dealer buys a painting for £45 and sells it for £72.
What percentage profit is this?

Profit = £72 − £45 = £27

Percentage profit = $\frac{27}{45} \times 100 = 60\%$

EXAMPLE 3

The value of a computer drops from £1200 to £700 in a year.
What percentage decrease is this?

Decrease in value = £1200 − £700 = £500

Percentage decrease = $\frac{500}{1200} \times 100 = 41.7\%$ to 1 decimal place

Increase by a percentage

To increase £240 by 23% you first work out 23% of £240.

£240 × 0·23 = £55·20

Then you add £55·20 to £240.

£240 + £55·20 = £295·20

There is a quicker way to do the same calculation.

To increase a quantity by 23% you need to find the original quantity plus 23%.

You know that 23% of a number means $\frac{23}{100} \times$ the number.

Similarly, 100% of a number means $\frac{100}{100} \times$ the number, which is the same as the number itself.

So to increase £240 by 23% you need to find 100% of £240 plus 23% of £240.

This is the same as 123% of £240.

So the calculation can be done in one stage.

£240 × 1·23 = £295·20

The number that you multiply the original quantity by (here 1·23) is called the **multiplier**.

▌ EXAMPLE 4

Amir's salary is £17 000 per year. He receives a 3% increase.
Find his new salary.

Amir's new salary is 103% of his original salary. So the multiplier is 1·03.

£17 000 × 1·03 = £17 510

Decrease by a percentage

You can calculate a percentage decrease in a similar way.

EXAMPLE 5

Kieran buys a DVD recorder in the sale.
The original price was £225.
Calculate the sale price.

A percentage decrease of 15% is the same as

100% − 15% = 85%.

So the multiplier is 0·85.

£225 × 0·85 = £191·25

SALE
15% OFF
EVERYTHING!

EXERCISE 2.2

1 A shopkeeper buys an article for £10 and sells it for £12.
What percentage profit does she make?

2 Adam earned £5 per hour. His pay increased to £5·60 per hour.
What was the percentage increase in Adam's pay?

3 A season ticket for Weston United normally costs £500 but if it is bought before 1 June it costs £360.
What percentage reduction is this?

4 Karl bought a CD for £12·50. A year later he sold it for £6.
What percentage of the value did he lose?

5 A shopkeeper buys an article for £22 and sells it for £28.
What is his percentage profit? Give your answer to the nearest 1%.

6 Hannah reduces the time it takes her to swim 30 lengths from 55 minutes to 47 minutes.
What percentage reduction is this? Give your answer to the nearest 1%.

7 Write down the multiplier that will increase an amount by each of these percentages.
a) 13%   **b)** 20%
c) 68%   **d)** 8%
e) 2%   **f)** 17·5%
g) 150%

8 Write down the multiplier that will decrease an amount by each of these percentages.
a) 14%   **b)** 20%
c) 45%   **d)** 7%
e) 3%   **f)** 23%
g) 16·5%

9 Sanjay used to earn £4·60 per hour from his Saturday job. He received a 4% increase.
How much does he earn now? Give your answer to the nearest penny.

EXERCISE 2.2 continued

10 In a sale, everything is reduced by 30%.
Abi buys a pair of shoes in the sale.
The original price was £42.
What is the sale price?

11 Ghalib's gas bill is £340 before VAT is
added on.
What is the bill after VAT at 5% is
added on?

12 A shop increases its prices by 8%.
What is the new price of a skirt which
previously cost £30?

13 In a sale, all the prices are reduced by
20%.
What is the sale price of an electric
shaver which previously cost £27?

ACTIVITY 3

VAT (Value Added Tax) is a tax added on to the price of goods and services.

a) Find out the current rate of VAT.

b) Write the current rate of VAT as a fraction and as a decimal.

CHALLENGE 1

The price of a camera is increased by 30%. Later, in a sale, the new price is reduced
by 20%.

What percentage change is the sale price as compared to the original price?

KEY IDEAS

■ To change a fraction to a decimal, divide the numerator by the denominator.

■ $\dfrac{a}{b} = a \div b$

■ To change a decimal to a percentage, multiply by 100.

■ To increase a quantity by 5%, for example, a quick way is to multiply the quantity by
1·05 (since 100 + 5 = 105).

■ To reduce a quantity by 12%, for example, a quick way is to multiply the quantity by
0·88 (since 100 − 12 = 88).

STAGE
7

3 Ratio and proportion

You will learn about

- Using ratios in proportion calculations
- Dividing a quantity in a given ratio
- Comparing proportions

You should already know

- How to multiply and divide without a calculator
- How to find common factors
- How to simplify fractions
- What is meant by an enlargement
- How to change between metric units
- About ratio and its notation
- How to write a ratio in its lowest terms
- How to write a ratio in the form $1:n$

Ratios with different units

A ratio is used to compare two or more quantities.
Sometimes you have to change the units of one part of the ratio first.

EXAMPLE 1

Write each of these ratios in its lowest terms.

a) 1 millilitre : 1 litre

b) 1 kilogram : 200 grams

a) 1 millilitre : 1 litre = 1 millilitre : 1000 millilitres
= 1 : 1000

Write each part in the same units.
When the units are the same, you do not need to include them in the ratio.

b) 1 kilogram : 200 grams = 1000 grams : 200 grams
= 5 : 1

Write each part in the same units.
Divide each part by 200.

EXAMPLE 2

Write each of these ratios in its lowest terms.

a) 50p : £2

b) 2 cm : 6 mm

c) 600 g : 2 kg : 750 g

a) 50p : £2 = 50p : 200p
= 1 : 4

Write each part in the same units.
Divide each part by 50.

b) 2 cm : 6 mm = 20 mm : 6 mm
= 10 : 3

Write each part in the same units.
Divide each part by 2.

c) 600 g : 2 kg : 750 g = 600 g : 2000 g : 750 g
= 12 : 40 : 15

Write each part in the same units.
Divide each part by 50.

EXERCISE 3.1

1 Write each of these ratios in its lowest terms.
 a) 6 : 16
 b) 15 : 24
 c) 48 : 60
 d) 24 : 36 : 40
 e) 36 : 18 : 30

2 Write each of these ratios in its lowest terms.
 a) 150 g : 1 kg
 b) £1·20 : £2
 c) 5 minutes : 1 minute 30 seconds
 d) 2 m : 60 cm
 e) 600 ml : 3 litres

3 At a concert there are 240 men and 560 women.
Write the ratio of men to women in its lowest terms.

4 Julie, Peter and Amy give £1·50, £6 and £2·40 respectively to charity.
Write the ratio of their donations in its lowest terms.

5 A recipe for leek and bacon casserole uses 2 kg of potatoes, 800 g of bacon and 1·4 kg of leeks.
Write the ratio of the ingredients in its lowest terms.

C CHALLENGE 1

Write each of these ratios in its simplest form.

a) 20 miles : 20 kilometres

b) 30 kilograms : 30 pounds

c) 40 litres : 40 gallons

Using ratios

Sometimes you know one of the quantities in the ratio, but not the other.

If the ratio is in the form 1 : n, you can work out the second quantity by multiplying the first quantity by n. You can work out the first quantity by dividing the second quantity by n.

EXAMPLE 3

a) The negative of a photo is enlarged in the ratio 1 : 20 to make a picture.
The negative measures 36 mm by 24 mm.
What size is the enlargement?

b) Another 1 : 20 enlargement measures 1000 mm × 1000 mm.
What size is the negative?

a) The enlargement will be 20 times bigger than the negative, so multiply both dimensions by 20.

$36 \times 20 = 720$
$24 \times 20 = 480$

The enlargement measures 720 mm by 480 mm.

b) The negative will be 20 times smaller than the negative, so divide the dimensions by 20.

$1000 \div 20 = 50$

The negative measures 50 mm × 50 mm.

EXAMPLE 4

A map is drawn to a scale of 1 cm : 2 km.

a) On the map, the distance between Amhope and Didburn is 5·4 cm.
What is the real distance in kilometres?

b) The length of a straight railway track between two stations is 7·8 km.
How long is this track on the map in centimetres?

a) The real distance, in kilometres, is twice as large as the map distance, in centimetres.
So multiply by 2.

2 × 5·4 = 10·8

Real distance = 10·8 km

b) The map distance, in centimetres, is half of the real distance, in kilometres.
So divide by 2.

7·8 ÷ 2 = 3·9

Map distance = 3·9 cm

C CHALLENGE 2

What would the answer to part **a)** of Example 4 be in centimetres?

What ratio could you use to work this out?

Sometimes you have to work out quantities using a ratio that is not in the form $1 : n$.

To work out an unknown quantity, you multiply each part of the ratio by the same number to get an equivalent ratio which contains the quantity you know. This number is called the **multiplier**.

EXAMPLE 5

To make jam, fruit and sugar are mixed in the ratio 2 : 3.

This means that if you have 2 kg of fruit, you need 3 kg of sugar.
If you have 4 kg of fruit, you need 6 kg of sugar.

How much sugar do you need for each of these amounts of fruit?
a) 6 kg   **b)** 10 kg   **c)** 500 g

a) 6 ÷ 2 = 3   Divide the quantity of fruit by the 'fruit' part of the ratio to
                               find the multiplier.
    2 : 3 = 6 : 9   Multiply each part of the ratio by the multiplier, 3.
    You need 9 kg of sugar.

b) 10 ÷ 2 = 5   Divide the quantity of fruit by the 'fruit' part of the ratio to
                               find the multiplier.
    2 : 3 = 10 : 15   Multiply each part of the ratio by the multiplier, 5.
    You need 15 kg of sugar.

c) 500 ÷ 2 = 250   Divide the quantity of fruit by the 'fruit' part of the ratio to
                               find the multiplier.
    2 : 3 = 500 : 750   Multiply each part of the ratio by the multiplier, 250.
                You need 750 g of sugar.

EXAMPLE 6

Two photos are in the ratio 2 : 5.

a) What is the height of the larger
photo?

b) What is the width of the smaller
photo?

8 cm

15 cm

a) 8 ÷ 2 = 4   Divide the height of the smaller photo by the smaller part of
                              the ratio to find the multiplier.
    2 : 5 = 8 : 20   Multiply each part of the ratio by the multiplier, 4.
                Height of the larger photo = 20 cm

b) 15 ÷ 5 = 3   Divide the width of the larger photo by the larger part of the
                              ratio to find the multiplier.
    2 : 5 = 6 : 15   Multiply each part of the ratio by the multiplier, 3.
                Width of the smaller photo = 6 cm

EXAMPLE 7

To make grey paint, white paint and black paint are mixed in the ratio 5 : 2.

a) How much black paint is mixed with 800 ml of white paint?

b) How much white paint is mixed with 300 ml of black paint?

A table is often useful for this sort of question.

	Ratio	5 of white	2 of black
a)	Amount	800 ml	2 × 160 = 320 ml
b)	Amount	5 × 150 = 750 ml	300 ml

Multiplier = 800 ÷ 5 = 160
Multiplier = 300 ÷ 2 = 150

a) You need 320 ml of black paint.

b) You need 750 ml of white paint.

EXAM TIP
Make sure you haven't made a silly mistake by checking that the bigger side of the ratio has the bigger quantity.

EXAMPLE 8

To make stew for four people, a recipe uses 1·6 kg of beef.

How much beef is needed using the same recipe for six people?

The ratio of people is 4 : 6.

4 : 6 = 2 : 3 — Write the ratio in its lowest terms.

1·6 ÷ 2 = 0·8 — Divide the quantity of beef needed for four people by the smaller part of the ratio to find the multiplier.

0·8 × 3 = 2·4 — Multiply the larger part of the ratio by the multiplier, 0·8.

2·4 kg of beef is needed for six people.

STAGE 7

EXERCISE 3.2

1 The ratio of the lengths of the sides of two squares is 1 : 6.
   a) The length of the side of a small square is 2 cm.
   What is the length of the side of the large square?
   b) The length of the side of a large square is 21 cm.
   What is the length of the side of the small square?

2 The ratio of helpers to babies in a crèche must be 1 : 4.
   a) There are six helpers on Tuesday. How many babies can there be?
   b) There are 36 babies on Thursday. How many helpers must there be?

3 Sanjay is mixing pink paint. To get the shade he wants, he mixes red and white paint in the ratio 1 : 3.
   a) How much white paint should he mix with 2 litres of red paint?
   b) How much red paint should he mix with 12 litres of white paint?

4 The negative of a photo is 35 mm long. An enlargement of 1 : 4 is made. What is the length of the enlargement?

5 A road atlas of Great Britain is to a scale of 1 inch to 4 miles.
   a) On the map, the distance between Forfar and Montrose is 7 inches. What is the real distance between the two towns in miles?
   b) It is 40 miles from Newcastle to Middlesbrough. How far is this on the map?

6 For a recipe, Chelsy mixes water and lemon curd in the ratio 2 : 3.
   a) How much lemon curd should she mix with 20 ml of water?
   b) How much water should she mix with 15 teaspoons of lemon curd?

7 To make a solution of a chemical, a scientist mixes 3 parts of the chemical with 20 parts of water.
   a) How much water should he mix with 15 ml of the chemical?
   b) How much of the chemical should he mix with 240 ml of water?

8 An alloy is made by mixing 2 parts of silver with 5 parts of nickel.
   a) How much nickel must be mixed with 60 g of silver?
   b) How much silver must be mixed with 120 g of nickel?

9 Sachin and Rehan share a flat. They agree to share the rent in the same ratio as their wages. Sachin earns £600 a month and Rehan earns £800 a month.
   If Sachin pays £90, how much does Rehan pay?

10 A recipe for hotpot uses onions, carrots and stewing steak in the ratio 1 : 2 : 5 by mass.
   a) What quantity of steak is needed if 100 g of onion is used?
   b) What quantity of carrots is needed if 450 g of steak is used?

Dividing a quantity in a given ratio

ACTIVITY 1

Maya has an evening job making up party bags for a children's party organiser. She shares out lemon sweets and raspberry sweets in the ratio 2 : 3. Each bag contains five sweets.

a) On Monday Maya makes up 10 party bags.
   (i) How many sweets does she use in total?
   (ii) How many lemon sweets does she use?
   (iii) How many raspberry sweets does she use?

b) On Tuesday Maya makes up 15 party bags.
   (i) How many sweets does she use in total?
   (ii) How many lemon sweets does she use?
   (iii) How many raspberry sweets does she use?

What do you notice?

A ratio represents the number of shares into which a quantity is divided.

The total number of shares the quantity is divided into is found by adding the parts of the ratio together.

To find the quantities shared in a ratio:

■ Find the total number of shares.
■ Divide the total quantity by the total number of shares to find the multiplier.
■ Multiply each part of the ratio by the multiplier.

> **EXAM TIP**
> The multiplier may not be a whole number. Work with the decimal or fraction and round the final answer if necessary.

STAGE

7

EXAMPLE 9

To make fruit punch, orange juice and grapefruit juice are mixed in the ratio 5 : 3.

Jo wants to make 1 litre of punch.

a) How much orange juice does she need, in millilitres?

b) How much grapefruit juice does she need, in millilitres?

5 + 3   = 8   First work out the total number of shares.
1000 ÷ 8 = 125   Convert 1 litre to millilitres and divide by 8 to find the multiplier.

A table is often helpful for this sort of question.

	Orange	Grapefruit
Ratio	5	3
Amount	5 × 125 = 625 ml	3 × 125 = 375 ml

a) She needs 625 ml of orange juice.

b) She needs 375 ml of grapefruit juice.

> ### EXAM TIP
> To check your answers, add the parts together. Together they should equal the total quantity.
>
> For example, 625 ml + 375 ml = 1000 ml ✓

EXERCISE 3.3

 Do not use your calculator for questions **1** to **5**.

1 Share £20 between Dave and Sam in the ratio 2 : 3.

2 Paint is mixed in the ratio 3 parts red to 5 parts white to make 40 litres of pink paint.
　　a) How much red paint is used?
　　b) How much white paint is used?

3 Asif is making mortar by mixing sand and cement in the ratio 5 : 1.
　　How much sand is needed to make 36 kg of mortar?

4 To make a solution of a chemical, a scientist mixes 1 part of the chemical with 5 parts of water. She makes 300 ml of the solution.
　　a) How much of the chemical does she use?
　　b) How much water does she use?

5 Amit, Bree and Chris share £1600 between them in the ratio 2 : 5 : 3. How much does each receive?

EXERCISE 3.3 continued

 You may use your calculator for questions **6** to **8**.

6 There are 572 senators in a national assembly. The numbers of senators in the Blue, Orange and Green parties are in the ratio 6 : 3 : 2.
How many senators are there in each of the parties?

7 St. Anthony's College Summer Fayre raised £1750. The governors decided to share the money between the college and a local charity in the ratio 5 : 1. How much did the local charity receive? Give your answer correct to the nearest pound.

8 Sally makes breakfast cereal by mixing bran, currants and wheat germ in the ratio 8 : 3 : 1 by mass.
a) How much bran does she use to make 600 g of the cereal?
b) One day, she has only 20 g of currants.
How much cereal can she make? She has plenty of bran and wheat germ.

The best value

A ACTIVITY 2

Two packets of cornflakes are available at a supermarket.

Which is the better value for money?

STAGE

7

To compare value, you need to compare *either*

- how much you get for a certain amount of money *or*
- how much a certain quantity (for example, volume or mass) costs.

In each case you are comparing **proportions**, either of size or of cost.

The better value item is the one with the **lower unit cost** or the **greater number of units per penny** (or per pound).

EXAMPLE 10

Sunflower oil is sold in 700 ml bottles for 95p and in 2 litre bottles for £2·45.

Show which bottle is the better value.

Method 1
Work out the price per millilitre for each bottle.

	Small	Large
Capacity	700 ml	2 litres = 2000 ml
Price	95p	£2·45 = 245p
Price per ml	95 ÷ 700 = 0·14p	245 ÷ 2000 = 0·1225p = 0·12p

Use the same units for each bottle.

Round your answers to 2 decimal places if necessary.

The price per ml is lower for the 2 litre bottle.
It has the lower unit cost. In this case the unit is a millilitre.
The 2 litre bottle is the better value.

Method 2
Work out the amount per penny for each bottle.

	Small	Large
Capacity	700 ml	2 litres = 2000 ml
Price	95p	£2·45 = 245p
Amount per penny	700 ÷ 95 = 7·37 ml	2000 ÷ 245 = 8·16 ml

Again, use the same units for each bottle.

Round your answers to 2 decimal places if necessary.

The amount per penny is greater for the 2 litre bottle.
It has the greater number of units per penny.
The 2 litre bottle is the better value.

EXAM TIP
Make it clear whether you are working out the cost per unit or the amount per penny, and include the units in your answers. Always show your working.

EXERCISE 3.4

1 A 420 g bag of Choco bars costs £1·59 and a 325 g bag of Choco bars costs £1·09.
Which is the better value for money?

2 Spa water is sold in 2 litre bottles for 85p and in 5 litre bottles for £1·79.
Show which is the better value.

3 Wallace bought two packs of cheese, a 680 g pack for £3·20 and a 1.4 kg pack for £5·40.
Which was the better value?

4 One-inch nails are sold in packets of 50 for £1·25 and in packets of 144 for £3·80.
Which packet is the better value?

5 Toilet rolls are sold in packs of 12 for £1·79 and in packs of 50 for £7·20.
Show which is the better value.

6 Brillowhite toothpaste is sold in 80 ml tubes for £2·79 and in 150 ml tubes for £5·00.
Which size tube is the better value?

7 A supermarket sell cola in three different sized bottles: a 3 litre bottle costs £1·99, a 2 litre bottle costs £1·35 and a 1 litre bottle costs 57p.
Which bottle gives the best value?

8 Crispy cornflakes are sold in three sizes: 750 g for £1·79, 1.4 kg for £3·20 and 2 kg for £4·89.
Which packet gives the best value?

C CHALLENGE 3

Here are some special offers at two discount music stores.

Explain which is the better offer if you want to buy

a) three CDs. **b)** four CDs.

STAGE

7

K KEY IDEAS

- If a ratio is in the form 1 : *n*, you can work out the second quantity by multiplying the first quantity by *n*. You can work out the first quantity by dividing the second quantity by *n*.

- To find an unknown quantity, each part of the ratio must be multiplied by the same number, called the multiplier.

- To divide a quantity in a given ratio, first find the total number of shares, then divide the total quantity by the total number of shares to find the multiplier. You can then multiply each part of the ratio by the multiplier.

- To compare value, work out either the cost per unit or the number of units per penny (or per pound). The better value item is the one with the lower cost per unit or the greater number of units per penny (or per pound).

Probability

You will learn about

- Finding the probability of an event *not* occurring
- Expected frequency
- The link between relative frequency and probability

You should already know

- That probabilities can be expressed as fractions, decimals or percentages
- That the total of the probabailities of all the mutually exclusive outcomes of an event is one
- How to simplify fractions

Theoretical probability

This section brings together much of the previous work you have done on probabilities.

We can often use a theoretical argument to work out probabilities. For example, when you toss a coin, it can land heads or tails. If the coin is not biased, these outcomes are equally likely. So the probability of getting a head is $\frac{1}{2}$.

This may be written more concisely as P(head) $= \frac{1}{2}$.

Where there is a set of equally likely outcomes,

$$\text{the probability of an event occurring} = \frac{\text{number of ways the event can occur}}{\text{total number of possible outcomes}}.$$

▌ EXAMPLE 1

What is the probability of drawing a red counter out of a box containing three blue, eight red and seven white counters?

Total number of counters = 18
Number of red counters = 8
Assuming that all the counters are equally likely to be chosen, P(red) $= \frac{8}{18} = \frac{4}{9}$.

In Example 1 we assumed that all the counters were equally likely to be chosen. This may be signalled by words in a question such as 'drawn out without looking' or 'drawn at random'. They are all ways of indicating that there is no special bias in the way the counter is drawn out.

You may also need to use the result that all probabilities add up to 1. In Example 1, for instance, P(a counter is not red) = $1 - P(\text{red}) = \frac{5}{9}$.

> **P(not A) = 1 – P(A)**

EXERCISE 4.1

1 When a fair dice is thrown, what is the probability of getting
  a) a 5?
  b) a prime number?
  c) an even number?
  d) a number which is divisible by 3?

2 A fair pentagonal spinner labelled 1, 2, 3, 4, 5 is spun.
What is the probability of getting
  a) a 5?
  b) a prime number?

3 The faces of a fair dice are labelled 1, 1, 2, 3, 4, 5.
For this dice, what is the probability of getting
  a) an even number?
  b) a number which is divisible by 3?

4 The probability that it will rain today is 0·85.
What is the probability that it will not rain today?

5 A pack of ordinary playing cards contains 52 cards.
What is the probability of drawing the ace of spades if one card is chosen at random?

6 A box of chocolates contains nine plain, five milk and six white chocolates.
One of these is taken at random.
Find the probability of taking
  a) a plain chocolate.
  b) a chocolate that is not white.

7 Sam's pencil case contains three red, four blue and five black pens. He takes a pen out without looking.
What is the probability that it is
  a) blue?
  b) green?

8 The probability of Cheryl winning a race is 0·2.
What is the probability that she doesn't win?

9 A pack of ordinary playing cards contains 52 cards.
What is the probability of drawing a heart if one card is chosen at random?

10 A box contains 12 red, 20 green and 8 yellow sweets. One sweet is taken at random.
Find the probability that the sweet is
  a) green.
  b) not red.

11 Tim's sock drawer has six pairs of black socks, four pairs of navy socks and five pairs of patterned socks. He takes out a pair without looking.
What is the probability that the pair is
  a) navy?
  b) white?

12 A 1p and a 10p piece are tossed together.
List all the possible outcomes and find the probability of getting two heads.

13 Two dice are thrown together.
List all the possible outcomes and
calculate the probability of getting
a) a double 6.
b) a score with a total of 10.

14 The probability that Adam's mum will
cook dinner tonight is $\frac{7}{10}$.
What is the probability that she will
not cook dinner?

15 The probability that Alec will watch
TV on Tuesday is $\frac{32}{49}$.
What is the probability that he will not
watch TV?

16 A bag contains black, red and blue
counters. Ben picks a counter without
looking.
The probability of picking a red
counter is 0·3 and the probability of
picking a black counter is 0·5.
What is the probability of picking a
blue counter?

17 Rebecca always comes to school on
her scooter, on her bicycle or walks.
On any day, the probability that
Rebecca will ride her bicycle to school
is $\frac{5}{19}$ and the probability that she will
scoot to school is $\frac{3}{19}$.
What is the probability that Rebecca
will walk to school?

18 The probability that the school
football team will win their next match
is 0·3. The probability that they will
lose is 0·45.
What is the probability that they will
draw the match?

19 Terry drinks either juice, coffee or tea.
The probability that he will have juice
is $\frac{3}{20}$ and the probability that he will
have coffee is $\frac{11}{20}$.
What is the probability that he will
have tea?

20 The table shows the probability of
getting some of the scores when a
biased six-sided dice is thrown.

Score	Probability
1	0·21
2	0·18
3	
4	0·15
5	0·23
6	0·12

What is the probability of getting a 3?

C CHALLENGE 1

The table shows the probability of getting each of the scores when a biased five-sided
spinner is spun.

Score	1	2	3	4	5
Probability	c	$2c$	$3c$	$2c$	c

Work out the probability of obtaining each score.

**STAGE
7**

Expected frequency

You can also use probability to predict how often an outcome will occur, or the **expected frequency** of the outcome.

EXAMPLE 2

Each time Ronnie plays a game of snooker, the probability that he will win is $\frac{7}{10}$.

In a season, Ronnie plays 30 games.

How many of the games can he be expected to win?

$P(\text{win}) = \frac{7}{10}$

This probability tells us that, on average, Ronnie will win seven times in every ten games he plays. That is, he will win $\frac{7}{10}$ of the time.

In a season, he can be expected to win $\frac{7}{10}$ of the 30 games.

$\frac{7}{10} \times 30 = \frac{210}{10} = 21$

This is an example of an important result.

Expected frequency = probability × number of trials

EXAMPLE 3

The probability of a child catching measles is 0·2.

There are 400 children in a primary school.

How many of them might you expect to catch measles?

Expected frequency = probability × number of trials
= 0·2 × 400
= 80 children

The number of 'trials' means the number of times the probability is tested.
Here, each of the 400 children has a 0·2 chance of catching measles. The number of trials is the same as the number of children, that is 400.

EXERCISE 4.2

1 The probability that Beverley is late for work is 0·1.
How many times would you expect her to be late in 40 working days?

2 The probability that it will be sunny on any day in April is $\frac{2}{5}$.
On how many of April's 30 days would you expect it to be sunny?

3 The probability that United will win their next match is 0·85.
How many of their next 20 games might you expect them to win?

4 When John is playing darts, the probability that he will hit the bull's eye is $\frac{3}{20}$.
John takes part in a sponsored event for charity. Each dart that hits the bull's eye will earn £5 for charity. John throws 400 darts.
How much might he expect to earn for charity?

5 An ordinary six-sided dice is thrown 300 times.
How many times might you expect it to score
a) 5?
b) an even number?

6 A box contains two yellow balls, three blue balls and five green balls. A ball is chosen at random, its colour is noted, and then it is replaced in the box. This is done 250 times.
How many of each colour might you expect to get?

7 Four cards are numbered 1, 2, 3 and 4. A card is chosen at random 40 times.
How many times would you expect to get a 4?

8 The probability of someone, chosen at random, being left-handed is 0·35.
In a school of 200 students, how many might you expect to be left-handed?

9 The probability that any child born has blood group O is $\frac{9}{20}$.
In the next 500 births, how many might you expect to have blood group O?

10 An unbiased coin is tossed 66 times.
How many heads might you expect to get?

C CHALLENGE 2

Two unbiased coins are tossed together 1000 times.

How many times might you expect to get two heads?

STAGE
7

Relative frequency and probability

It is not always possible to find probabilities from looking at equally likely outcomes. For example, you may have to work out the probability of throwing a 6 with a dice that may be biased, the probability of a young driver having an accident, or the probability that a person will visit a certain supermarket.

For this type of event you need to set up some sort of experiment, carry out a survey or look at past results.

Take the example of throwing a 6 with a dice that may be biased.
For a fair (unbiased) dice, the probability of getting a six is
$\frac{1}{6} = 0.166... = 0.17$ approximately.

If you were to throw it ten times and get four 6s, would this be evidence of bias?

The proportion of sixes is $\frac{4}{10} = 0.4$ which is very different from 0.17, but in a small sample of trials there may be runs of non-typical results. So you would not conclude that the dice was biased.

What about 10 times in 50 throws? Here the proportion is $\frac{10}{50} = 0.2$ which is still quite a bit different from 0.17, but again you have not thrown it enough times to be sure. So you still would not conclude that the dice was biased.

What about 108 times in 600 throws? You have thrown the dice a large number of times and the proportion of 6s is $\frac{108}{600} = 0.18$. This is too close to 0.17 to conclude that the dice was biased, now that you have thrown it so many times.

What about 100 times in 500 throws? Now you have thrown the dice a large number of times and the proportion is $\frac{100}{500} = 0.2$. This is significantly different from 0.17, but not so much that you should conclude that the dice is biased.

The important question is, how many trials are necessary to ensure a representative result?

There is no fixed answer to this, other than 'the more the better'.

As a general rule, any event being examined should occur at least 100 times, but even this is probably a bare minimum.

In the case of a 6 occurring 100 times in 500 throws, the proportion of 6s is $\frac{100}{500}$. This fraction is called the **relative frequency**.

$$\text{Relative frequency} = \frac{\textbf{number of times an outcome occurs}}{\textbf{total number of trials}}$$

This is a measure of the proportion of the trials in which the outcome occurs. It is not itself a measure of probability. If, however, the number of trials is large enough, relative frequency can be used as an estimate of probability.

Remember that, no matter how many trials have taken place, relative frequency is still only an estimate, but in many cases it is the only method of estimating probability.

A ACTIVITY 1

Copy this table and complete it by following the instructions below.

Number of trials	20	40	60	80	100
Number of heads					
Relative frequency = $\dfrac{\text{number of heads}}{\text{number of trials}}$					

- ■ Toss a coin 20 times and use tally marks to record the number of times it lands heads.

- ■ Now toss the coin another 20 times and enter the number of heads for all 40 tosses.

- ■ Continue in groups of 20 and record the number of heads for 60, 80 and 100 tosses.

- ■ Calculate the relative frequency of heads for 20, 40, 60, 80 and 100 tosses. Give your answers to 2 decimal places.

a) What do you notice about the values of the relative frequencies?

b) The probability of getting a head with one toss of a coin is $\frac{1}{2}$ or 0·5. Why is this?

c) How does your final relative frequency value compare with 0·5?

EXAMPLE 4

Ian carries out a survey on the colours of the cars passing his school.
His results are shown in this table.

Colour	Black	Red	Blue	White	Green	Other	Total
Number of cars	51	85	64	55	71	90	416

Use these figures to estimate the probability that the next car that passes will be

a) red. **b)** not red.

Since the number of trials is large, use relative frequency as an estimate of probability.

a) Relative frequency of a red car $= \frac{85}{416}$

Estimate of probability $= \frac{85}{416}$ or 0·204 (to 3 decimal places)

b) $416 - 85 = 331$

Relative frequency $= \frac{331}{416}$

Estimate of probability $= \frac{331}{416}$ or 0·796 (to 3 decimal places)

A ACTIVITY 2

Perform an experiment or conduct a survey to test one of
these hypotheses.

■ Every dice is unbiased so that the probability of
getting any number is $\frac{1}{6}$.

■ The probability of a boy or girl
being born is the same, $\frac{1}{2}$.

Hint: Select
a dice that you think
has been very unfair to you,
throw it as many times as you
can and estimate the
probability of getting
a 1, a 2, a 3 ...

Hint: Gather
your data from your school
by asking each student to state the
genders of the members of their family
(or your local hospital might give you
information from the recent birth
records). Estimate the probability
of a boy or a girl birth.

EXERCISE 4.3

1 Use the figures from Ian's survey in Example 4 to estimate the probability that the next car will be
a) blue.
b) black or white.
Give your answers correct to 3 decimal places.

2 Kim Lee tossed a coin ten times and it came down heads eight times. Kim Lee said that the coin was biased towards heads.
Explain why she may not be right.

3 Solomon has a spinner in the shape of a pentagon with sides labelled 1, 2, 3, 4, 5. Solomon spun the spinner 500 times. The results are shown in the table.

Number on spinner	Number of times
1	102
2	103
3	98
4	96
5	101

a) What is the relative frequency of scoring
(i) 2?   **(ii)** 4?
b) Do the results suggest that Solomon's spinner is fair?
Explain your answer.

4 In an experiment, a drawing pin is thrown. It can land either point up or point down. It lands point up 87 times in 210 throws.
Use these figures to estimate the probability that, the next time it is thrown, it will land
a) point up.
b) point down.
Give your answers correct to 2 decimal places.

5 Denise carried out a survey about crisps. She asked 400 people in the town where she lived which was their favourite flavour of crisps. The results are shown in this table.

Flavour	Number of people
Ready salted	150
Salt and vinegar	75
Cheese and onion	55
Prawn cocktail	50
Other	70

a) Explain why it is reasonable to use these figures to estimate the probability that the next person Denise asks will choose salt and vinegar.
b) Use the figures to estimate the probability that the next person Denise asks will choose
(i) salt and vinegar.
(ii) ready salted.
Give your answers as fractions in their simplest form.

6 An insurance company finds that 203 drivers out of 572 in the age range 17–20 have an accident in the first year after passing their driving test.
Use these figures to estimate the probability that a driver aged 17–20 will have an accident in the first year after passing their test.

7 While Tom is standing at the bus stop he notices that five out of the 20 cars he sees passing are Fords. He says that therefore the probability that the next car will be a Ford is $\frac{1}{4}$.
Explain why he is wrong.

EXERCISE 4.3 continued

8 Freya carries out a survey to find out how students in her school travel to school. She asks a random selection of 200 students. The results are shown in this table.

Method of travel	Number of students
Bus	34
Car	33
Train	23
Cycle	45
Walk	65

a) Explain why it is reasonable to estimate the probabilities of students travelling by the various methods from this survey.

b) Use these figures to estimate the probability that a student selected at random from the school
(i) travels by bus.
(ii) cycles.

9 Noel has two coins which he suspects may be biased.

a) He tosses the first coin 600 times and throws 312 heads.
Is there evidence to suggest that this coin is biased? Give your reasons.
If there is, estimate the probability that the next throw is a head.

b) He tosses the second coin 600 times and throws 420 heads.
Is there evidence to suggest that this coin is biased? Give your reasons.
If there is, estimate the probability that the next throw is a head.

10 The table shows the results of a survey on the type of detergent households use to do their washing.

Type of detergent	Number of households
Liquid	120
Powder	233
Tablets	85

Use these figures to estimate, correct to 2 decimal places, the probability that the next household surveyed will use
a) liquid.
b) tablets.

11 Stewart made a five-sided spinner. Unfortunately he did not make the pentagon regular. In order to find the probability of getting each of the numbers, he spun the spinner 400 times. His results are shown in this table.

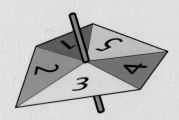

Number	Frequency
1	63
2	84
3	101
4	57
5	95

Use the figures in the table to estimate the probability of the spinner landing on
a) 1.
b) 3.
c) an even number.

EXERCISE 4.3 continued

12 A shopkeeper noticed from his till roll that, out of 430 customers that day, 82 had spent over £10.
Use these figures to estimate the probability that his next customer will spend £10 or less.

13 Murphy's Law states that when you drop a piece of toast, it will land buttered side down nine times out of ten.
Describe carefully an experiment you could carry out to test Murphy's Law.

CHALLENGE 3

Work in pairs.

Put ten counters, some red and the rest white, into a bag.

Challenge your partner to work out how many counters there are of each colour.

> **Hint:** You need to devise an experiment with 100 trials. At the start of each trial, all ten counters must be in the bag.

KEY IDEAS

■ Where there is a set of equally likely outcomes,

$$\text{the probability of an event occurring} = \frac{\text{number of ways the event can occur}}{\text{total number of possible outcomes}}.$$

■ P(not A) = 1 − P(A)

■ Relative frequency = $\dfrac{\text{number of times an event occurs}}{\text{total number of trials}}$

■ If the number of trials is large enough, relative frequency can be used as an estimate of probability.

STAGE

7

Using and generating formulae

Letters for unknowns

Imagine you had a job where you were paid by the hour. You would receive the same amount for each hour you worked.

How could you work out how much you will earn in a week?

You would need to work it out as the number of hours you worked multiplied by the amount you are paid for each hour

This is a formula in words.

If you work 35 hours at £4·50 an hour, it is easy to work out 35 × £4·50, but what if the numbers change? The calculation '35 × £4·50' is only correct if you work 35 hours. Suppose you move to another job where you are paid more for each hour.

You need a simple formula that *always* works. You can use symbols to stand for the numbers that can change.

You could use ? or □, but it is less confusing to use letters.

Let   the number of hours worked be N
           the amount you are paid each hour be P
           the amount you earn in a week be W.
Then $W = N \times P$.

EXAMPLE 1

Use the formula $W = N \times P$ to find W when $N = 40$ and $P = £5.00$.

$W = N \times P$
$= 40 \times 5$
$= £200$

Some rules of algebra

■ You do not need to write the $\times$ sign.
$4 \times t$ is written $4t$.

■ In multiplications, the number is always written in front of the letter.
$p \times 6 - 30$ is written $6p - 30$.

■ You often start a formula with the single letter you are finding.
$2 \times l + 2 \times w = P$ is written $P = 2l + 2w$.

■ When there is a division in a formula, it can be written as a fraction.
$y = k \div 6$ can be written $y = \dfrac{k}{6}$.

EXAMPLE 2

When you make a journey, S is the speed, d is the distance travelled and t is the time taken. Write a formula for S.

To find the speed, you divide the distance by the time, so the formula for S is
$S = d \div t$ or $S = \dfrac{d}{t}$.

EXAM TIP

If you are not sure whether to multiply or divide, try an example with numbers first.

EXAMPLE 3

The cost (C) of hiring a car is a fixed charge (f), plus the number of days (n) multiplied by the daily rate (d). Write a formula for C.

$C = f + n \times d$ or $C = f + nd$

STAGE

7

EXERCISE 5.1

Write a formula for each of these, using the letters given.

1 The cost (C) of x pencils at y pence each.

2 The area (A) of a rectangle m cm long and n cm wide.

3 The height (h) of a stack of n tins each t cm high.

4 The temperature in °F (F) is 32, plus 1·8 times the temperature in °C (C).

5 My gas bill (B) is a charge (s), plus the number (n) of units used multiplied by the cost (u) of each unit.

6 The mileage performance (R, the number of miles per litre) of a car is the number (m) of miles travelled divided by the number (p) of litres of petrol used.

7 The time (T) to cook a turkey is 40 minutes for each kilogram (k) plus 30 minutes.

8 The area (A) of a triangle is half the base (b) times the height (h).

9 The number of dollars (d) is 1·65 times the number of pounds (p).

10 The current in a circuit (I) is the voltage (V) divided by the resistance (R).

11 The cost (£C) of hiring a car for n days at a rate of £40 per day plus a basic charge of £12.

12 The cost (£C) of n units of electricity at 12p per unit, plus a standing charge of £6.

13 The hire charge (£C) for a car is £28 multiplied by the number of days (d), plus a fixed charge of £15.

14 The area (A) of a semicircle is approximately 1·6 multiplied by the square of the radius (r).

15 The area (A) of an ellipse is π multiplied by its length (a) and its width (b).

16 The cost of petrol (C) is the number of litres (n) multiplied by the price of petrol per litre (p).

17 The total of the wages (w) in a factory is the number of workers (n) multiplied by the weekly wage (q).

18 The perimeter (p) of a quadrilateral is the sum of the lengths of its sides (a, b, c, d).

19 The cost (P) of n books at q pounds each.

20 The number of books (N) that can fit on a shelf is the length (L) of the shelf divided by the thickness (t) of each book.

21 The time (t) for a journey is the distance (d) divided by the speed (s).

22 The number of euros (E) is 1·5 times the number of pounds (P).

23 The number of posts (Q) for a fence is the length of the fence (R) divided by 2, plus 1.

24 The number of eggs (n) in a box a eggs across, b eggs along and c eggs up.

25 The approximate circumference (C) of a circle is 6 multiplied by its radius (r).

26 The cost (£C) of n CDs at £7·50 each and v videos at £12 each.

EXERCISE 5.1 continued

27 The cost (£C) of n minutes of mobile phone use at 30p per minute, plus a rental charge of £14.

28 The area (A) of a kite is half the product of the width (w) and the length (m).

29 The density (d) of an object is its mass (m) divided by its volume (v).

30 The final velocity (v) of an object moving with constant acceleration (a) is the product of the time taken (t) and the acceleration, plus the start velocity (u).

Before you do Exercise 5.2, check your answers to Exercise 5.1.

EXERCISE 5.2

Use the formulae in Exercise 5.1 to find each of these.

1 C when $x = 15$ and $y = 12$

2 A when $m = 7$ and $n = 6$

3 h when $n = 20$ and $t = 17$

4 F when $C = 40$

5 B when $s = 9{\cdot}80$, $n = 234$ and $u = 0{\cdot}065$

6 R when $m = 320$ and $p = 53{\cdot}2$

7 T when $k = 9$

8 A when $b = 5$ and $h = 6$

9 d when $p = 200$

10 I when $V = 13{\cdot}6$ and $R = 2{\cdot}5$

11 C when $n = 5$

12 C when $n = 532$

13 C when $d = 5$

14 A when $r = 5$

15 A when $a = 3$ and $b = 2$

16 C when $n = 50$ and $p = 70$

17 w when $n = 200$ and $q = 150$

18 p when $a = 7$, $b = 5$, $c = 8$ and $d = 2$

19 P when $n = 25$ and $q = 7$

20 N when $L = 90$ and $t = 3$

21 t when $d = 260$ and $s = 40$

22 E when $P = 50$

23 Q when $R = 36$

24 n when $a = 12$, $b = 20$ and $c = 6$

25 C when $r = 5$

26 C when $n = 2$ and $v = 3$

27 C when $n = 80$

28 A when $w = 40$ and $m = 60$

29 d when $m = 200$ and $v = 25$

30 v when $u = 6$, $a = 1{\cdot}5$ and $t = 8$

STAGE

7

C CHALLENGE 1

For this triangle, $h^2 = a^2 + b^2$.

a) Find h in each of these cases.
   (i) $a = 3$ and $b = 4$
   (ii) $a = 5$ and $b = 12$
   (iii) $a = 4 \cdot 2$ and $b = 7 \cdot 1$

b) Find a when $h = 25$ and $b = 24$.

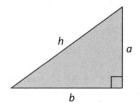

Using harder numbers and formulae

Numbers to be substituted in a formula may be positive, negative, decimals or fractions.

> **EXAM TIP**
>
> Take special care when negative numbers are involved.

EXAMPLE 4

$W = 4p - 5q^2$. Find W in each of these cases.

a) $p = 2$ and $q = {}^-3$

b) $p = 22 \cdot 5$ and $q = 3 \cdot 4$

c) $p = \frac{3}{4}$ and $q = \frac{2}{5}$

> **EXAM TIP**
>
> Remember that $5b^2$ means $5 \times b \times b$, not $5 \times b \times 5 \times b$.

a) $W = (4 \times 2) - (5 \times {}^-3 \times {}^-3)$
   $= 8 - (5 \times 9)$
   $= 8 - 45$
   $= {}^-37$

> **EXAM TIP**
>
> Work out each term separately and then collect together.

b) $W = (4 \times 22 \cdot 5) - (5 \times 3 \cdot 4 \times 3 \cdot 4)$
   $= 90 - 57 \cdot 8$
   $= 32 \cdot 2$

In part **b)** you would use a calculator.

c) $W = \left(4 \times \frac{3}{4}\right) - \left(5 \times \frac{2}{5} \times \frac{2}{5}\right)$
   $= 3 - \frac{4}{5}$
   $= 2\frac{1}{5}$

STAGE
7

EXAMPLE 5

The formula for the surface area of a cylinder is $S = 2\pi rh + 2\pi r^2$.

Find the surface area when $r = 5.7$ and $h = 4.6$.
Give your answer to the nearest whole number.

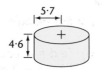

$S = (2 \times \pi \times 5.7 \times 4.6) + (2 \times \pi \times 5.7^2)$
  $= 164.745... + 204.140...$
  $= 368.885...$
$S = 369$ (to the nearest whole number)

EXAM TIP

Use the π key on your calculator. Write down the intermediate values but leave them in your calculator to avoid making errors by rounding too early.

EXAMPLE 6

$S = ut + \frac{1}{2}at^2$. Find S when $u = 3$, $t = 4$ and $a = {}^-5$.

$S = (3 \times 4) + \left(\frac{1}{2} \times {}^-5 \times 4^2\right) = 12 - 40 = {}^-28$

EXAMPLE 7

$P = ab + 4b^2$. Find P when $a = \frac{4}{5}$ and $b = \frac{3}{8}$, giving your answer as a fraction.

$P = \left(\frac{4}{5} \times \frac{3}{8}\right) + \left(4 \times \frac{3}{8} \times \frac{3}{8}\right) = \frac{3}{10} + \frac{9}{16} = \frac{24}{80} + \frac{45}{80} = \frac{69}{80}$

EXERCISE 5.3

Work out each of the formulae in questions **1** to **14** for the values given. Do not use your calculator.

1 $V = ab - ac$ when $a = 3$, $b = {}^-2$ and $c = 5$

2 $P = 2rv + 3r^2$ when $r = 5$ and $v = {}^-2$

3 $T = 5s^2 - 2t^2$ when $s = {}^-2$ and $t = 3$

4 $M = 2a(3b + 4c)$ when $a = 5$, $b = 3$ and $c = {}^-2$

5 $R = \dfrac{2qv}{q + v}$ when $q = 3$ and $v = {}^-4$

6 $L = 2n + m$ when $n = \frac{2}{3}$ and $m = \frac{5}{6}$

7 $D = a^2 - 2b^2$ when $a = \frac{4}{5}$ and $b = \frac{2}{5}$

8 $A = a^2 + b^2$ when $a = 5$ and $b = {}^-3$

9 $P = 2c^2 - 3cd$ when $c = 2$ and $d = {}^-5$

10 $B = p^2 - 3q^2$ when $p = {}^-4$ and $q = {}^-2$

11 $T = (4a - 5b)^2$ when $a = {}^-2$ and $b = {}^-1$

12 $Q = x(y^2 - z^2)$ when $x = {}^-2$, $y = 7$ and $z = {}^-3$

13 $S = ab + 5b^2$ when $a = \frac{3}{4}$ and $b = \frac{4}{5}$

14 $R = a + 2b$ when $a = 1\frac{5}{6}$ and $b = \frac{2}{3}$

STAGE
7

You may use your calculator for questions **15** to **20**.

15 Find the value of $M = \dfrac{ab}{(2a + b^2)}$

when $a = 2.75$ and $b = 3.12$.
Give your answer correct to 2 decimal places.

16 The distance S metres fallen by a pebble is given by the formula $S = \frac{1}{2}gt^2$, where t is in seconds.

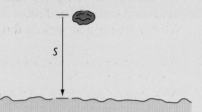

Find S in each of these cases.
a) $g = 10$ and $t = 12$
b) $g = 9.8$ and $t = 2.5$

17 The surface area of a cuboid with sides x, y and z is given by the formula $A = 2xy + 2yz + 2xz$.

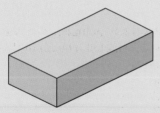

Find the surface area when $x = 5$, $y = 4.5$ and $z = 3.5$.

18 The elastic energy of an elastic string is given by the formula $E = \dfrac{\lambda x^2}{2a}$.
Find E when $\lambda = 3.4$, $x = 5.7$ and $a = 2.5$. Give your answer correct to 1 decimal place.

19 The area of cross-section of a tree trunk is given by the formula $A = \dfrac{P^2}{4\pi}$ where P is the distance round the trunk.

Find the area of cross-section when $P = 56\,\text{cm}$. Give your answer correct to the nearest $10\,\text{cm}^2$.

20 The focal length of a lens is given by the formula $f = \dfrac{uv}{u + v}$.
Find the focal length when $u = 6$ and $v = {}^{-}7$.

STAGE 7

K KEY IDEAS

EXAM TIP
Remembering the word BIDMAS may help.

■ When you have substituted numbers in a formula and are working out the result, remember the order of operations – brackets and indices (powers), then divide and multiply, then add and subtract.

Revision exercise A1

1 Find the coordinates of the midpoint of the line joining each of these pairs of points. Try to do it without plotting the points.
a) A(2, 1) and B(4, 7)
b) C(2, 3) and D(6, 8)
c) E(2, 0) and F(7, 9)

2 The diagram shows the outline of a house.

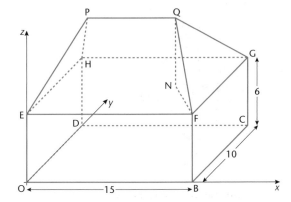

All the measurements are in metres.
All the walls are vertical.
E, F, G, H and N are in the same horizontal plane.
a) Write down the coordinates of each of these points.
  (i) B
  (ii) H
  (iii) G

The coordinates of Q are (11, 5, 9).
N is vertically below Q.
b) Write down the coordinates of N.

3 Change each of these fractions to a decimal. Give your answers correct to 3 decimal places.
a) $\frac{5}{16}$
b) $\frac{4}{7}$
c) $\frac{7}{40}$
d) $\frac{4}{15}$

4 Change each decimal you found in question **3** into a percentage. Give your answers correct to 1 decimal place.

5 Karl cuts 20 cm from a piece of wood 1·6 m long.
By what percentage has he shortened the piece of wood?

6 The audience for a TV soap increased from 8 million to 10 million.
What percentage increase is this?

7 The number of students in a school went down from 850 to 799.
What percentage reduction is this?

8 Write down the multiplier that will increase an amount by each of these percentages.
a) 15%
b) 30%
c) 9%
d) 7·5%
e) 120%

9 Write down the multiplier that will decrease an amount by each of these percentages.
a) 12%
b) 40%
c) 58%
d) 2%
e) 4·5%

10 In a sale all prices are reduced by 15%. Find the new price of a pair of trainers that originally cost £65.

11 The value of an antique increased by 20%. The antique was originally worth £450.
What is it worth now?

12 Write each of these ratios in its simplest form.
  a) 50 : 35
  b) 30 : 72
  c) 1 minute : 20 seconds
  d) 45 cm : 1 m
  e) 600 ml : 1 litre

13 To make 12 scones Maureen uses 150 g of flour.
  How much flour does she use to make 20 scones?

14 To make a fruit and nut mixture, raisins and nuts are mixed in the ratio 5 : 3 by mass.
  a) What mass of nuts is mixed with 100 g of raisins?
  b) What mass of raisins is mixed with 150 g of nuts?

15 Peter made a fruit punch by mixing orange, lemon and grapefruit juices in the ratio 5 : 1 : 2.
  a) He made a 2 litre bowl of fruit punch. How many millilitres of grapefruit juice did he use?
  b) How much fruit punch could he make with 150 ml of orange juice?

16 Show which is the better buy, 5 litres of oil for £18·50 or 2 litres of oil for £7·00.

17 Supershop sells milk in pints at 43p and in litres at 75p.
  One pint is equal to 568 ml.
  Which is the better buy?

18 A fair octagonal spinner is numbered 1 to 8.
  When it is spun, what is the probability of getting
  a) a number greater than 5?
  b) a multiple of 3?

19 An unbiased coin is tossed and a normal dice is thrown.
  What is the probability of getting both a head and a 6?

20 The probability that Jane wears red clothes is $\frac{3}{10}$.
  What is the probability that she doesn't wear red?

21 A box contains five milk, six plain and four white chocolates. Chris picks one out at random.
  What is the probability that he gets a plain chocolate? Give your answer as a fraction in its lowest terms.

22 The probability that City win their next game is 0·55 and the probability that they lose their next game is 0·3.
  What is the probability that they draw their next game?

23 The probability of picking a black counter from a box of counters is $\frac{1}{6}$. Sue makes 300 selections from the box.
  How many times might you expect her to pick a black counter?

24 The probability that United win any match is 0·85.
  In a season of 40 matches, how many might you expect United to win?

25 Over the last year Rebecca has been late for school 25 times in 190 days.
  Use these figures to estimate the probability that she will be on time the next school day. Give your answer correct to 2 decimal places.

26 The ages of the drivers of the last 250 cars to have crashes at an 'accident black spot' are shown in this table.

Age (years)	Number of crashes
17–20	40
21–24	35
25–49	105
50–64	45
65 and over	25

a) Use the table to estimate the probability that the next driver to have a crash at the black spot will be aged
  (i) 25–49.
  (ii) over 65.
b) Explain why these figures do not necessarily mean that drivers aged 65 and over are the safest.

27 Rachel has a four-sided spinner with the sides numbered 1, 2, 3 and 4. She wants to test whether the spinner is a fair one. Describe carefully how you would advise her to do this.

28 Pencils cost 20p each.
Write an expression for the cost of x pencils.

29 The posters in a sale all cost the same price. Tracey bought eight posters for £a. Write an expression for the cost of one poster.

30 Anna has t coins in her purse. Rebecca has four more than Anna, Sian has two fewer than Anna, and Jessica has twice as many as Anna.
Write an expression for the number of coins each of these women has.
a) Rebecca
b) Sian
c) Jessica

31 To convert temperatures on the Celsius (°C) scale to the Fahrenheit (°F) scale you can use the formula $F = 1.8C + 32$. Convert each of these temperatures to Fahrenheit.
a) 40 °C
b) 0 °C
c) ⁻5 °C

32 The cost of a child's bus ticket is half the adult fare plus 25p.
a) Write an expression for the cost of a child's ticket.
b) Find the cost of a child's ticket when the adult fare is £1·40.

33 The area of a rhombus is found by multiplying the lengths of the diagonals together and then dividing by 2.
a) Write an expression for the area of a rhombus.
b) Find the area of a rhombus with diagonals of length
  (i) 4 cm and 6 cm.
  (ii) 5·4 cm and 8 cm.

34 $P = a^2 + b^2$
a) Find P when $a = 4$ and $b = 7$.
b) Find P when $a = 3$ and $b = 4$.
c) Find P when $a = ⁻3$ and $b = ⁻4$.

35 $h = 7a - 2bc$
a) Find h when $a = 2$, $b = 3$ and $c = ⁻1$.
b) Find h when $a = \frac{1}{4}$, $b = \frac{1}{2}$ and $c = \frac{3}{4}$.
c) Find h when $a = 3·6$, $b = 7·4$ and $c = 2·5$.

STAG
7

6 Solving angle problems

This chapter brings together all the angle facts you have already met and gives you practice in using them to solve problems.

Lines, points, triangles and quadrilaterals

You need to know and be able to solve problems using these angle facts.

- Angles on a straight line add up to 180°.
- Angles round a point add up to 360°.
- When two straight lines cross, the opposite angles are equal.
- Angles in a triangle add up to 180°.
- Angles in a quadrilateral add up to 360°.
- In an isosceles triangle, the angles opposite the equal sides are themselves equal.

EXAMPLE 1

Find angle x. Give a reason for your answer.

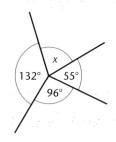

x = 360° – (132° + 55° + 96°)   Angles around a point add
  = 77°   up to 360°.

EXERCISE 6.1

1   Find the size of each lettered angle in
    these diagrams, giving your reasons.

a)

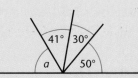

b)

c)

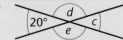

d)

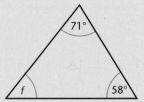

e)

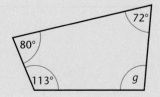

f)

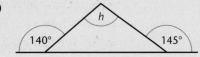

g)

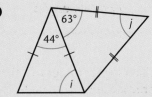

h)

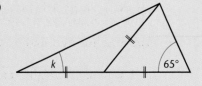

2   Three angles of a quadrilateral are 62°,
    128° and 97°.
    Calculate the size of the other angle.

3   Three angles of a quadrilateral are 57°,
    132° and 76°.
    Calculate the size of the other angle.

4   An isosceles triangle has one angle
    of 108°.
    Calculate the size of the other two
    angles.

STAGE
7

C CHALLENGE 1

An isosceles triangle has an angle of 40°. Find the sizes of the other two angles in the triangle. There are two possible answers – find both sets of two angles.

C CHALLENGE 2

A quadrilateral is divided into two triangles, as shown in the diagram.

Prove that the interior angles of a quadrilateral add up to 360°.

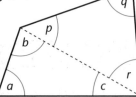

Parallel lines

You need to know and be able to solve problems using the angle facts relating to parallel lines.

> **EXAM TIP**
> Thinking of a Z shape may help you remember this – or looking at the diagrams upside-down and seeing the same shapes.

■ **Alternate angles** are equal.

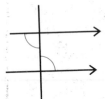 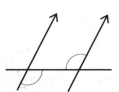 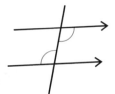 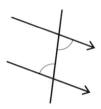

> **EXAM TIP**
> Thinking of an F shape or a translation may help you remember this.

■ **Corresponding angles** are equal.

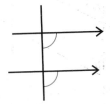 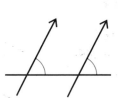 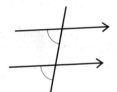 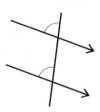

■ **Allied angles** add up to 180°.

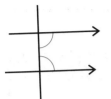
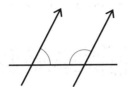
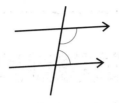
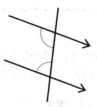

A ACTIVITY 1

This is a map of part of New York.

a) Find Broadway and W 32nd Street on the map.
Find some more angles equal to the angle between Broadway and W 32nd Street.

b) Two angles that add up to 180° are called **supplementary**. Find an angle that is supplementary to the angle between Broadway and W 32nd Street.

c) Explain your results.

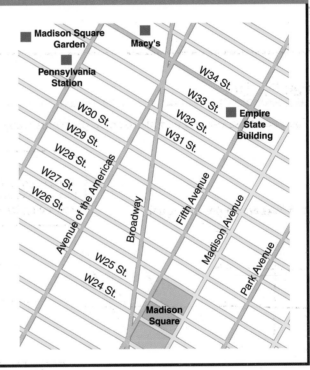

EXAMPLE 2

Find the size of each lettered angle, giving your reasons.

$a = 116°$ Angles on a straight line add up to 180°.
$b = 64°$ Corresponding angles or co-interior angles.
$c = 64°$ Vertically opposite angles.

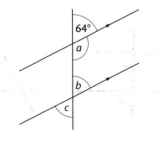

EXERCISE 6.2

Find the size of each lettered angle, giving your reasons.

1

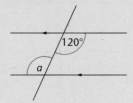

2

3

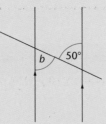

4

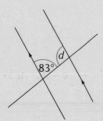

5

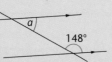

6

7

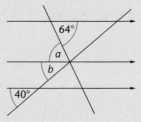

8

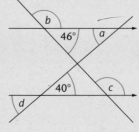

9

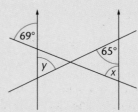

10

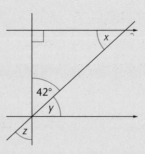

Find the value of x. Give a reason for each step of your work.

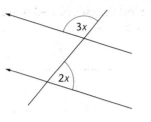

Angles in polygons

You need to know and be able to solve problems using the angle facts relating to polygons.

For any convex polygon

- The sum of all the exterior angles is 360°.
- The interior angle + the exterior angle = 180°.

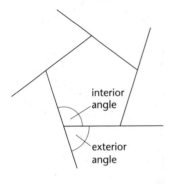

interior angle

exterior angle

For an *n*-sided polygon

- The sum of the interior angles = $180° \times (n - 2)$

This means that

- The sum of the interior angles of a triangle is 180°.
- The sum of the interior angles of a quadrilateral is 360°.
- The sum of the interior angles of a pentagon is 540°.
- The sum of the interior angles of a hexagon is 720°.

For any regular polygon

- All the interior angles are equal, all the exterior angles are equal, and all the sides are equal.
- Each exterior angle = $\dfrac{360°}{\text{number of sides}}$
- Each interior angle = 180° – exterior angle
- The angle at the centre = $\dfrac{360°}{\text{number of sides}}$

STAGE

7

EXAMPLE 3

Find the value of x in this hexagon.

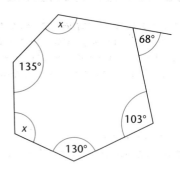

First, find the size of the missing interior angle.
Interior angle + exterior angle = 180°
Interior angle = 180° – 68°
            = 112°

Next, find the sum of the interior angles.
Sum of interior angles = 112° + 103° + 130° + 135° + 2x
                = 480° + 2x

The sum of the interior angles of a hexagon = 720°, therefore
480° + 2x = 720°
      2x = 720° – 480°
       = 240°
      x = 120°

EXAMPLE 4

Find the interior angle of a regular hexagon.

For a regular hexagon, the exterior angle = 360° ÷ 6 = 60°.
So the interior angle = 180° – 60° = 120°.

EXAMPLE 5

Find the number of sides of a regular polygon with an interior angle of 144°.

If the interior angle = 144°,
the exterior angle   = 180° – 144°
            = 36°.
The sum of the exterior angles = 360°.

Therefore the number of sides = 360° ÷ 36° = 10.

C CHALLENGE 4

A shape will tessellate if a number of copies of the shape will fit together on a flat surface without any gaps. Regular octagons do not tessellate but, as this picture of a tiled floor shows, regular octagons and squares may be combined to cover a surface.

Can you find
a) which regular polygons tessellate?
b) which combinations of regular polygons will cover a surface?

▌▌▌ EXERCISE 6.3

1 Three of the exterior angles of a quadrilateral are 90°, 52° and 87°. Find the size of the other exterior angle.

2 Four of the exterior angles of a pentagon are 70°, 59°, 83° and 90°.
   a) Find the size of the other exterior angle.
   b) Find the size of each interior angle.

3 Five of the exterior angles of a hexagon are 54°, 48°, 65°, 35° and 80°.
   a) Find the size of the other exterior angle.
   b) Find the size of each interior angle.

4 Three of the exterior angles of a quadrilateral are 110°, 61° and 74°. Find the size of the other exterior angle.

5 Four of the exterior angles of a pentagon are 68°, 49°, 82° and 77°.
   a) Find the size of the other exterior angle.
   b) Find the size of each interior angle.

6 Four of the exterior angles of a hexagon are 67°, 43°, 91° and 37°.
   a) Find the size of the other exterior angles, given that they are equal.
   b) Find the size of each interior angle.

7 A regular polygon has nine sides. Find the size of each of its exterior and interior angles.

8 Find the interior angle of a regular dodecagon (12 sides).

9 A regular polygon has an exterior angle of 24°. How many sides does it have?

10 What is the sum of the interior angles of
   a) a hexagon?
   b) a decagon?

11 Six of the angles of a heptagon are 122°, 141°, 137°, 103°, 164° and 126°. Calculate the size of the remaining angle.

12 A regular polygon has 15 sides. Find the size of each of its exterior and interior angles.

13 Find the size of the interior angle of a regular 20-sided polygon.

14 A regular polygon has an exterior angle of 30°. How many sides does it have?

STAGE

7

Solving angle problems

15 What is the sum of the interior angles of
  a) an octagon?
  b) a nonagon?

16 A polygon has 11 sides. Ten of its interior angles add up to 1490°. Find the size of the remaining angle.

The exterior angle of a triangle

If one of the sides of a triangle is extended, to form an angle outside the triangle, this angle is called the **exterior angle**.

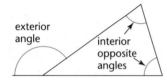

You need to know and be able to solve problems using this fact.

- The exterior angle of a triangle is equal to the sum of the interior opposite angles.

EXAMPLE 6

Work out the size of each lettered angle. Give a reason for each answer.

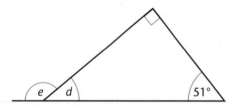

$d = 180° - (51° + 90°)$
$\quad = 39°$

Angles in a triangle add up to 180°.

$e = 51° + 90°$
$\quad = 141°$

The exterior angle of a triangle is equal to the sum of the interior opposite angles.

STAGE
7

EXERCISE 6.4

Calculate the size of each of the angles marked with a letter in these diagrams.

You may need to use some of the other angle facts you know to solve the problems in this exercise.

1

2

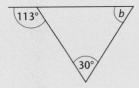

3

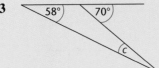

4

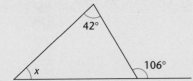

5

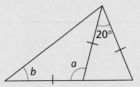

6

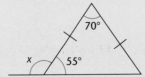

7

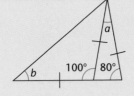

8

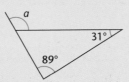

9

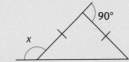

10

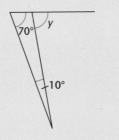

11

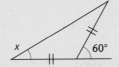

12

13

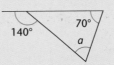

14

15

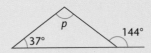

16

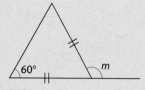

17

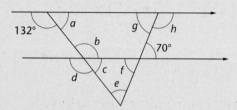

18

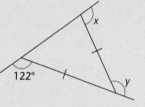

19

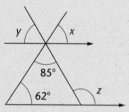

20

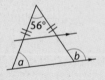

21

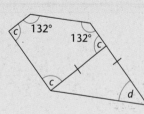

22

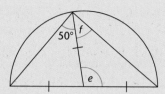

23

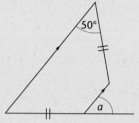

24

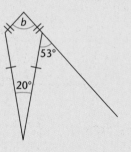

25

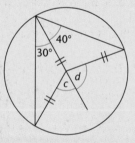

KEY IDEAS

Basic angle facts

■ Angles on a straight line add up to 180°.

■ Angles round a point add up to 360°.

■ When two straight lines cross, the opposite angles are equal.

■ Angles in a triangle add up to 180°.

■ Angles in a quadrilateral add up to 360°.

■ In an isosceles triangle, the angles opposite the equal sides are themselves equal.

Angles in parallel lines

■ Alternate angles are equal.

■ Corresponding angles are equal.

■ Allied angles add up to 180°.

Angles in polygons

■ The sum of the exterior angles of any convex polygon is 360°.

■ In any polygon, the interior angle and the exterior angle add up to 180°.

■ The sum of the interior angles of a triangle is 180°.

■ The sum of the interior angles of a quadrilateral is 360°.

■ The sum of the interior angles of a pentagon is 540°.

■ The sum of the interior angles of a hexagon is 720°.

■ The exterior angle of a regular polygon = $\dfrac{360°}{\text{number of sides}}$

■ The angle at the centre of a regular polygon = $\dfrac{360°}{\text{number of sides}}$

Exterior angle of a triangle

■ The exterior angle of a triangle is equal to the sum of the interior opposite angles.

Direct proportion

When quantities are in direct proportion, multiplication patterns can be seen if the quantities are put in a table. Using these patterns is often the easiest way of calculating unknown values.

There are multiplication patterns horizontally in the table when x and y are proportional. When x is doubled, so is y; when x is multiplied by 3, so is y; and so on.

$\times 2 \qquad \times 3$

x	4	8	24
y	10	20	60

$\times 2 \qquad \times 3$

There are also patterns vertically in the table. In this example, each y value is 2·5 times the corresponding x value. The equation connecting x and y is $y = 2·5x$.

x	4	8	24	
y	10	20	60	×2·5

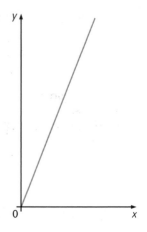

The graph of *y* against *x* is a straight line through the origin.
This is so for any two quantities in direct proportion.

The statement '*y* is directly proportional to *x*' is written in symbols as *y* ∝ *x*.

When *y* is directly proportional to *x* then the equation connecting *y* and *x* can be written as
y = *kx* where *k* is a constant.

EXAMPLE 1

Calculate the values of *p* and *q* in this table, where *a* and *b* are proportional.

a	3	p	12
b	18	54	q

$\frac{54}{18} = 3$, so $p = 3 \times 3 = 9$

$\frac{12}{3} = 4$, so $q = 18 \times 4 = 72$

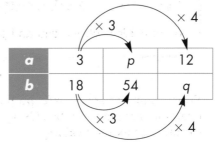

a	3	p	12
b	18	54	q

EXAMPLE 2

y and *x* are directly proportional. When *y* = 9, *x* = 2.

a) Find the equation connecting *y* and *x*.

b) **(i)** Find the value of *y* when *x* = 18.
  (ii) Find the value of *x* when *y* = 27.

a) When *y* ∝ *x*, the equation connecting *y* and *x* is *y* = *kx*.

  When *y* = 9, *x* = 2
  so   9 = 2*k*
          k = 4·5

  The equation connecting *y* and *x* is *y* = 4·5*x*.

b) **(i)** When *x* = 18,
          y = 4·5 × 18
             = 81

  (ii) When   *y* = 27,
          27 = 4·5*x*
  so $x = \frac{2·7}{4·5}$
             = 6

STAGE
7

EXERCISE 7.1

1 Copy and complete each of these tables, using multipliers.

a) $y \propto x$

x	6	12	30	
y	24			4

b) $p \propto q$

p	3	15		
q	18		12	30

c) $y \propto x$

x	2	4	20	
y	14			56

d) $p \propto q$

p	4	20	1	
q	20			75

2 Calculate the missing values in each of these tables, where y is proportional to x.

a)

x	4		20
y	10	30	

b)

x	5		20
y	30	6	

3 Calculate the missing value in each of these tables, where y is proportional to x. Find also the equation connecting y and x for each table.

a)

x	6	12	
y	30	60	80

b)

x	2	6	
y	15	45	90

4 Calculate the missing values in this table, where A is proportional to x. Find also the equation connecting A and x.

x	4	12	
A	18		90

5 Calculate the missing values in this table, where a is proportional to b. Find also the equation connecting a and b.

a	2	8	
b	7		105

6 A is proportional to r. When $r = 4$, $A = 6$.
Find the value of A when $r = 12$ and the value of r when $A = 30$.

7 C is proportional to x. When $x = 5$, $C = 8$.
Find the value of C when $x = 15$ and the value of x when $C = 20$.

8 $C \propto p$. When $p = 4$, $C = 18$.
Find the value of C when $p = 20$ and the value of p when $C = 63$.

9 C is proportional to m. When $m = 5$, $C = 12$.
Find the value of C when $m = 25$ and the value of m when $C = 18$.

10 a and b are directly proportional. When $a = 5$, $b = 6$.
Find the equation connecting a and b and the value of a when $b = 15$.

11 a and b are directly proportional. When $a = 12$, $b = 15$.
Find the equation connecting a and b and the value of a when $b = 20$.

12 Calculate the missing values in each of these tables, where y is proportional to x.

a)
x	12	-2	
y	18		6·9

b)
x	9	-3	
y	2·7		2·1

13 $y \propto x$. When $x = 4$, $y = 6·4$.
Find the equation connecting x and y and the value of x when $y = 56$.

14 $y \propto x$. When $x = 5$, $y = 27$.
Find the equation connecting x and y and the value of x when $y = 18·9$.

15 Complete this table to show the rate of conversion between dollars and pounds.

Pounds	3	12	25	
Dollars	4·50			180·00

16 According to its label, a 5 litre tin of paint covers 65 m². Use a table or conversion graph to find how many litres of paint are needed to cover the walls of a room with each of these areas.
a) 26 m²
b) 47 m²

17 A car goes 12·6 miles on 2 litres of petrol.
a) How much petrol does it need to go 84 miles?
b) How far can it go on 5 litres of petrol?

18 A 1500 g strawberry cheesecake to serve 8 people contains 210 g of strawberries.
How many grams of strawberries should there be in a cheesecake to serve 12 people?

C CHALLENGE 1

y is proportional to x^2. When $x = 5$, $y = 100$.

a) Find the equation connecting y and x.

b) (i) Find the value of y when $x = 7$.
(ii) Find the value of x when $y = 144$.

K KEY IDEAS

When two quantities x and y are in direct proportion:

■ Multiplication patterns can be seen if the quantities are put in a table. Using these patterns is often the easiest way of calculating unknown values.

■ There are multiplication patterns horizontally in the table when x and y are proportional. When x is doubled, so is y; when x is multiplied by 3, so is y; and so on.

■ There are also patterns vertically in the table. Each y value is k times its corresponding x value, for some number k. The equation connecting x and y is $y = kx$.

■ The graph of y against x is a straight line through the origin. This is so for any two quantities in direct proportion.

■ The statement 'y is directly proportional to x' is written in symbols as $y \propto x$.

STAGE
7

Checking solutions and calculations

You will learn about

- Using estimates to check the accuracy of your answer
- Finding an estimate of the answer to a problem

You should already know

- Basic numerical methods such as finding ratios and percentages
- How to round numbers to 1 significant figure

Checking your work

When you have solved a problem, how do you know if your answer is right?
Sometimes, accuracy is vital. There was a story in the news of a doctor treating a
baby. She put the decimal point in the wrong place in a calculation and prescribed
100 times as much of the drug as she intended.

Using common sense

Does your answer sound sensible in the context of the question? In practical
problems, your own experience often gives you an idea of the size of the answer
you expect. For example, in the case of a shopping bill, you would probably react
and check if it came to more than you expected!

Using number facts

A ACTIVITY 1

Multiplying
Starting with the number 400, multiply it by the numbers in each of these sets.

Set A:	5	1·1	3·2	1·003	1·4	1·2
Set B:	0·5	0·999	0·6	0·9	0·7	0·95

What happens to the number 400? Does it get bigger or smaller? What conclusions can you come to?

In particular, what happens when any number is multiplied by a number which is
a) greater than 1?
b) less than 1?
c) 1 itself?

Division
Repeat the activity, but divide instead of multiplying. Write down your conclusions.

In particular, what happens when any number is divided by a number which is
a) greater than 1?
b) less than 1?
c) 1 itself?

Look at the answer to this calculation.

$752 \div 24 = 18\,048$

When 752 is divided by a number that is greater than 1, the result should be less than 752.

Instead, it is more. It looks as if the $\times$ button was pressed by mistake, instead of the $\div$ button. Using number facts can help to spot errors like this.

Starting with any positive number,

- **multiplying by a number greater than 1 gives a result that is larger than the number**
- **multiplying by a positive number smaller than 1 gives a smaller result**
- **dividing by a number greater than 1 gives a smaller result**
- **dividing by a positive number smaller than 1 gives a larger result.**

Here are some other facts that you can use to check a calculation.

- **odd × odd = odd**   **even × odd = even**   **even × even = even**
- **+ × + = +**   **+ × − = −**   **− × − = +**
  and similarly for division
- **Multiplying any number by 5 will give a result that ends in 0 or 5.**
- **The last digit in a multiplication comes from multiplying the last digits of the numbers.**

Using inverse operations

Without a calculator, it is difficult to work out the square root of most numbers. However, if you know the square numbers, you can tell whether an answer is sensible.

EXAMPLE 1

Show how you can tell that the answer to this calculation is wrong.

$\sqrt{35} = 9 \cdot 52$ to 2 decimal places

$6^2 = 36$ so $\sqrt{35}$ must be less than 6.

Using inverse operations is also useful when you are using your calculator.

For example, if you work out $6 \cdot 9 \div 750 = 0 \cdot 0092$ using a calculator, you can check the answer by using your calculator to work out $0 \cdot 0092 \times 750 = 6 \cdot 9$.

Using estimates

Many people make estimates when they are shopping. They round prices to the nearest pound to make calculations easier.

EXAMPLE 2

Kate has £25 birthday money to spend. She sees CDs at £7·99.
How many of them can she buy?

You do not need to know the exact answer to $25 \div 7 \cdot 99$ so do a quick estimate.
Use £8 instead of £7·99.

$3 \times 8 = 24$ so $25 \div 8 = 3$ 'and a bit'.

So Kate can buy three CDs.

You can extend this idea to your maths lessons, and any other subjects where you use calculations.

STAGE
7

EXERCISE 8.1

1 Which of these answers might be correct and which are definitely wrong? Show how you decided.
a) $39.6 \times 18.1 = 716.76$
b) $175 \div 1.013 = 177.275$
c) $8400 \times 9 = 756\,000$
d) A lift takes 9 people, so a party of 110 people will need 12 trips.
e) Henry has £100 birthday money to spend and reckons that he can afford 5 DVDs costing £17.99 each.

e) $0.3^2 = 0.9$
f) $16.2 \div 8.1 = 20$
g) $125 \div 0.5 = 25$
h) $6.4 \times {}^-4 = 25.6$
i) $24.7 + 6.2 = 30.8$
j) $76 \div 0.5 = 38$
k) $({}^-0.9)^2 = {}^-0.81$
l) $\sqrt{1000} = 10$
m) $1.56 \times 2.5 = 0.39$
n) $360 \div 15 = 2400$

2 Look at these calculations. The answers are all wrong.
For each calculation, show how you can tell this quickly, without using a calculator to work it out.
a) $^-6.2 \div {}^-2 = {}^-3.1$
b) $12.4 \times 0.7 = 86.8$
c) $31.2 \times 40 = 124.8$
d) $\sqrt{72} = 9.49$ to 2 d.p.

3 Use estimates to calculate a rough total cost for each of these.
a) Seven packs of crisps at 22p each
b) Nine CDs at £13.25 each
c) 39 theatre tickets at £7.20 each
d) Five CDs at £5.99 and two tapes at £1.99
e) Three meals at £5.70 and two drinks at 99p

Rounding numbers to 1 significant figure

We often use rounded numbers instead of exact ones.

A ACTIVITY 2

Which of the numbers in these statements are likely to be exact, and which have been rounded?

a) Yesterday, I spent £14.62.

b) My height is 180 cm.

c) Her new dress cost £40.

d) The attendance at the Arsenal match was 32 000.

e) The cost of building the new school is £27 million.

f) The value of π is 3.142.

g) The Olympic Games were held in Athens in 2004.

h) There were 87 people at the meeting.

A ACTIVITY 3

Look for some examples of rounded and unrounded numbers in newspapers, magazines, advertising material and on TV.

Which, if any, of the rounded numbers do you think have been rounded up, and which have been rounded down? Why?

Can you think of any cases when someone might want to round figures up rather than down?

You should already know how to round numbers to 1 significant figure (1 s.f.). This means giving just one non-zero figure, with zeros as placeholders to make the number the correct size.

EXAMPLE 3

Round each of these numbers to 1 significant figure.

a) £29·95   **b)** 48 235   **c)** 0·072

a) £29·95 = £30 to 1 s.f.   The second non-zero digit is 9, so round the 2 up to 3.
Looking at place value, the 2 represents 20.
You use one zero to show the size.

b) 48 235 = 50 000 to 1 s.f.   The second non-zero digit is 8, so round the 4 up to 5.
Looking at place value, the 4 represents 40 000.
You use zeros to show the size.

c) 0·072 = 0·07 to 1 s.f.   The second non-zero digit is 2, so the 7 stays as it is.
Looking at place value, the 7 is 0·07, which stays as it is.

EXERCISE 8.2

Round each of these numbers to 1 significant figure.

1	8·2	**7**	967	**13**	14·9	**19**	0·58
2	6·9	**8**	0·43	**14**	167	**20**	0·037
3	17	**9**	0·68	**15**	21·2	**21**	1·0042
4	25·1	**10**	3812	**16**	794	**22**	20 053
5	493	**11**	4199	**17**	6027	**23**	0·069
6	7.0	**12**	3·09	**18**	0·013	**24**	1942

STAGE

7

Checking answers by rounding to 1 significant figure

It is important to be able to check calculations quickly, without using a calculator. One way to do this is to round the numbers to 1 significant figure and find an approximate answer to the calculation.

EXAMPLE 4

Find an approximate answer to the calculation 5.13×4.83.

$5.13 \times 4.83 \approx 5 \times 5 = 25$ Round each number to 1 s.f. to give a much simpler calculation.

EXAM TIP

In a multiplication it may be possible to round one number up and another number down. This might give an estimate that is closer to the exact answer.

EXERCISE 8.3

Find an approximate answer to each of the calculations in questions **1** to **39** by rounding each number to 1 significant figure. Show your working.

1   $31.3 \div 4.85$

2   113.5×2.99

3   $44.669 \div 8.77$

4   $3.6 \times 14.9 \times 21.5$

5   48.67×12.69

6   0.89×5.2

7   61.33×11.79

8   $(1.8 \times 2.9) \div 3.2$

9   $\dfrac{14.56 \times 22.4}{59.78}$

10   $\dfrac{4.9^2 \times 49.3}{96.7}$

11   $\sqrt{4.9 \times 5.2}$

12   $\dfrac{3.99}{0.8 \times 1.64}$

13   $198.5 \times 63.1 \times 2.8$

14   $\dfrac{\sqrt{8.1 \times 1.9}}{1.9}$

15   $(0.35 \times 86.3) \div 7.9$

16   $\sqrt{103.5} \div \sqrt{37.2}$

17   9.87×0.0657

18   $0.95 \div 4.8$

19   $32 \times \sqrt{124}$

20   $\dfrac{62 \times 9.7}{10.12 \times 5.1}$

21   0.246×0.789

22   $44.555 \div 0.086$

23   46×82

STAGE 7

24 $\sqrt{84}$

25 $\dfrac{1083}{8\cdot2}$

26 $7\cdot05^2$

27 $43\cdot7 \times 18\cdot9 \times 29\cdot3$

28 $\dfrac{2\cdot46}{18\cdot5}$

29 $\dfrac{29}{41\cdot6}$

30 917×38

31 $\dfrac{283 \times 97}{724}$

32 $\dfrac{614 \times 0\cdot83}{3\cdot7 \times 2\cdot18}$

33 $\dfrac{6\cdot72}{0\cdot051 \times 39\cdot7}$

34 $\sqrt{39 \times 80}$

35 $65\cdot4 \div 3\cdot9$

36 $\dfrac{194\cdot4 \div 3\cdot9}{27\cdot3}$

37 $\dfrac{49\cdot7}{4\cdot1 \times 7\cdot9}$

38 $3\cdot1 \times 14\cdot9$

39 $47 \times (21\cdot7 + 39\cdot2)$

40 At the school fete, Tony sold 245 ice-creams at 85p each. Estimate his takings.

41 A rectangle measures 5·8 cm by 9·4 cm. Estimate its area.

42 A circle has diameter 6·7 cm. Estimate its circumference. ($\pi = 3\cdot142...$)

43 A new car is priced at £14 995 excluding VAT. VAT at 17·5% must be paid on it. Estimate the amount of VAT to be paid.

44 A cube has sides of 3·7 cm. Estimate its volume.

45 Pedro drove 415 miles in 7 hours 51 minutes. Estimate his average speed.

ACTIVITY 4

Use a calculator to see how close your approximations in Exercise 8.3 questions **1** to **14** are to the correct answers.

CHALLENGE 1

Make up some multiplication and division calculations to test whether this statement is true.

'In multiplication and division calculations, rounding each number to 1 significant figure will always give an answer which is correct to 1 significant figure.'

Checking solutions and calculations

K KEY IDEAS

Check your work by doing at least one of these checks.

- Does the answer sound sensible in the context of the question?

- Do a quick estimate, for example by rounding each number to 1 significant figure.

- Do the calculation another way to check.

- Work backwards from your answer.

Scatter diagrams and correlation

9

A scatter diagram is used to find out whether there is a **correlation**, or relationship, between two sets of data. The data are presented as pairs of values, each of which is plotted as a coordinate point on a graph.

Here are some examples of what a scatter diagram could look like and how we might interpret them.

Strong positive correlation

Here, one quantity increases as the other increases.

This is called **positive correlation**.

The trend is from bottom left to top right.

When the points are closely in line, we say that the correlation is **strong**.

Weak positive correlation

These points also display positive correlation.

The points are more scattered, so we say that the correlation is **weak**.

Strong negative correlation

Here, one quantity decreases as the other increases.

This is called **negative correlation**.

The trend is from top left to bottom right.

Again, the points are closely in line, so we say that the correlation is **strong**.

Weak negative correlation

These points also display negative correlation.

The points are more scattered, so the correlation is **weak**.

No correlation

When the points are totally scattered and there is no clear pattern, we say that there is **no correlation** between the two quantities.

Scatter diagrams may also be called scatter graphs.

A   ACTIVITY 1

Do tall people have large feet?

Survey people in your class or in your year and record their height and foot size (foot length might be better than shoe size but either could be done).

Plot height on the horizontal axis and foot size on the vertical axis.

What do you notice? Try other year groups.

Lines of best fit

If a scatter diagram shows correlation, you can draw a **line of best fit** on it.

Try putting your ruler in various positions on the scatter diagram until you have a slope which matches the general slope of the points. There should be roughly the same number of points on each side of the line.

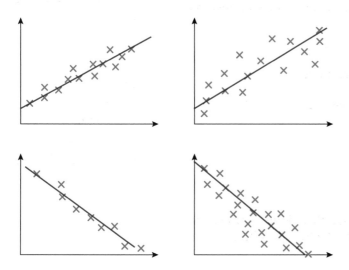

You cannot draw a line of best fit on a scatter diagram with no correlation.

You can use the line of best fit to predict a value when only one of the pair of quantities is known.

EXAMPLE 1

The table shows the heights and weights of 12 people.

Height (cm)	150	152	155	158	158	160	163	165	170	175	178	180
Weight (kg)	56	62	63	64	57	62	65	66	65	70	66	67

a) Draw a scatter diagram to show these data.

b) Comment on the strength and type of correlation between these heights and weights.

c) Draw a line of best fit on your scatter diagram.

d) Tom is 162 cm tall. Use your line of best fit to estimate his weight.

a), c)

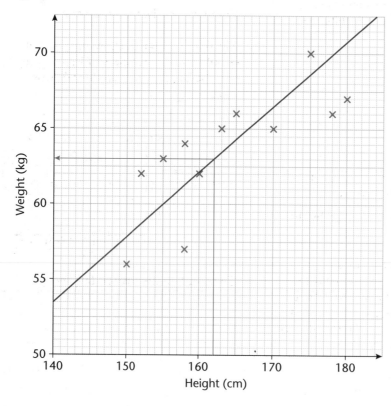

b) Weak positive correlation.

d) Draw a line up from 162 cm on the height axis to meet your line of best fit.
Now draw a horizontal line and read off the value where it meets the weight axis.
Tom's probable weight is about 63 kg.

1 The scatter diagram shows the numbers of sun beds hired out and the hours of sunshine at Brightsea.

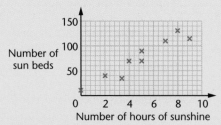

Comment on the results shown by the scatter diagram.

2 A firm noted the numbers of days of 'sick-leave' taken by its employees in a year, and their ages. The results are shown in the graph.

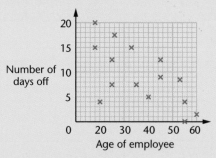

Comment on the results shown by the scatter diagram.

3 A teacher thinks that there is a correlation between how far back in class a student sits and how well they do at maths. To test this, she plotted their last maths grade against the row they sit in. Here is the graph she drew.

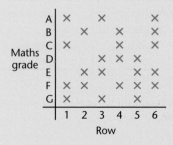

Was the teacher right? Give your reasons.

4 The scatter diagram shows the positions of football teams in the league and their mean crowd numbers, in thousands.

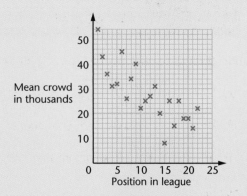

Comment on the scatter diagram.

5 The scatter diagram shows the ages of people and the numbers of lessons they took before they passed their driving tests.

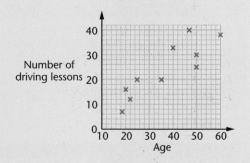

Comment on the scatter diagram.

6 The table shows the maths and science marks of eight students in their last examination.

Student	Maths mark	Science mark
A	10	30
B	20	28
C	96	80
D	50	55
E	80	62
F	70	70
G	26	38
H	58	48

a) Draw a scatter diagram to show this information, with the maths mark on the horizontal axis.
b) Comment on the diagram.
c) Draw a line of best fit.
d) Use your line of best fit to estimate
   (i) the science mark of a student who scored 40 in maths.
   (ii) the maths mark of a student who scored 75 in science.

7 The table shows the amount of petrol left in a fuel tank after different numbers of miles travelled.

Number of miles	Number of gallons
50	7
100	5·2
150	4·2
200	2·6
250	1·2
300	0·4

a) Draw a scatter diagram to show this information, with the number of miles on the horizontal axis.
b) Comment on the diagram.
c) Draw a line of best fit.
d) Use your line of best fit to estimate the number of gallons left after 170 miles.

8 In Kim's game, 20 objects are placed on a table and you are given a certain time to look at them. They are then removed or covered up and you have to recall as many as possible. The table shows the lengths of time given to nine people and the numbers of items they remembered.

Time in seconds	Number of items
20	9
25	8
30	12
35	10
40	12
45	15
50	13
55	16
60	18

a) Draw a scatter diagram to show this information, with time in seconds on the horizontal axis.
b) Comment on the diagram.
c) Draw a line of best fit.
d) Use your line of best fit to estimate the number of items remembered if 32 seconds are allowed.
e) Why should the diagram not be used to estimate the number of items remembered in 3 seconds?

9 In Jane's class, a number of students have part-time jobs. Jane thinks that the more time they spend on their jobs, the worse they will do at school. She asked ten of them how many hours a week they spent on their jobs, and found their mean marks in the last examinations. Her results are shown in the table.

Student	Time on part-time job (hours)	Mean mark in examination
A	9	50
B	19	92
C	13	52
D	3	70
E	15	26
F	20	10
G	5	80
H	17	36
I	6	74
J	22	24

a) Plot a scatter diagram to show Jane's results, with time in hours on the horizontal axis.
b) Do the results confirm Jane's views? Are there any exceptions?
c) Draw a line of best fit for the relevant points.
d) Estimate the mean score of a student who spent 12 hours on their part-time job.

10 In an experiment, Tom's reaction time is tested after he has undergone vigorous exercise. The table shows Tom's reaction times and the lengths of time spent in exercise.

Amount of exercise (minutes)	Reaction time (seconds)
0	0·34
10	0·46
20	0·52
30	0·67
40	0·82
50	0·91

a) Draw a scatter diagram to show this information, with the number of minutes of exercise on the horizontal axis.
b) Comment on the diagram.
c) Draw a line of best fit.
d) Use your line of best fit to estimate Tom's reaction time after 35 minutes of exercise.

11 The table shows the number of bad peaches per box after different delivery times.

Delivery time (hours)	Number of bad peaches
10	2
4	0
14	4
18	5
6	2

a) Draw a scatter diagram to show this information.
b) Describe the correlation shown in the scatter diagram.
c) Draw a line of best fit on your scatter diagram.
d) Use your line of best fit to estimate the number of bad peaches expected after a 12 hour delivery time.

STAGE
7

12 The table shows the marks of 15 students taking Paper 1 and Paper 2 of a maths examination. Both papers were marked out of 40.

Paper 1	Paper 2
36	39
34	36
23	27
24	20
30	33
40	35
25	27
35	32
20	28
15	20
35	37
34	35
23	25
35	33
27	30

a) Draw a scatter diagram to show this information.
b) Describe the correlation shown in the scatter diagram.
c) Draw a line of best fit on your scatter diagram.
d) Joe scored 32 on Paper 1 but was absent for Paper 2.
Use your line of best fit to estimate his score on Paper 2.

13 The table shows the engine size and petrol consumption of nine cars.

Engine size (litres)	Petrol consumption (mpg)
1·9	34
1·1	42
4·0	23
3·2	28
5·0	18
1·4	42
3·9	27
1·1	48
2·4	34

a) Draw a scatter diagram to show this information.
b) Describe the correlation shown in the scatter diagram.
c) Draw a line of best fit on your scatter diagram.
d) A tenth car has an engine size of 2·8 litres.
Use your line of best fit to estimate the petrol consumption of this car.

EXERCISE 9.1 continued

14 Tracy thinks that the larger your head, the cleverer you are. The table shows the number of marks scored in a test by each of ten students, and the circumference of their head.

Circumference of head (cm)	Mark
600	43
500	33
480	45
570	31
450	25
550	42
600	23
460	36
540	24
430	39

a) Draw a scatter diagram to show this information.

b) Describe the correlation shown in the scatter diagram.

c) Is Tracy correct?

d) Can you think of any reasons why the data may not be valid?

CHALLENGE 1

a) Dan thinks that the more time he spends on his school work, the less money he will spend. Sketch a scatter diagram that shows this.

b) Fiona thinks that the more she practises, the more goals she will score at hockey. Sketch a scatter diagram to show this.

CHALLENGE 2

Investigate one of these.

- Petrol consumption and the size of a car's engine
- A person's height and their head circumference
- House price and the distance from the town centre
- Age of car and second-hand price

STAGE 7

K KEY IDEAS

- Scatter diagrams show the correlation between two variables.

Perfect positive
correlation

Strong positive
correlation

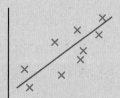

Weak positive
correlation

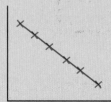

Perfect negative
correlation

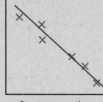

Strong negative
correlation

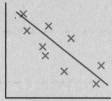

Weak negative
correlation

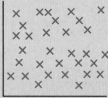

No correlation

- If there is reasonable correlation, a line of best fit can be drawn.

- The line of best fit should reflect the slope of the points.

- There should be approximately the same number of points on each side of the line.

- The line of best fit can be used to estimate the value of one variable if the other is known.

- The line of best fit can only be used to estimate values within the range of the given data.

STAGE

7

Pythagoras' theorem

Pythagoras' theorem

This is a square drawn on squared paper.
Its area is 4 square units.

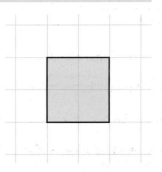

Here is a tilted square.
Calculating its area is more difficult. There are two methods you could use.

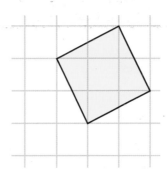

Pythagoras' theorem

1 Calculate the area of the large square drawn around the outside and subtract the area of the four shaded triangles.

Area = 9 – 1 – 1 – 1 – 1 = 5 square units

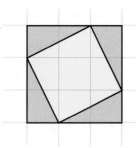

2 Add together the area of the four shaded triangles and the area of the middle square.

Area = 1 + 1 + 1 + 1 + 1 = 5 square units

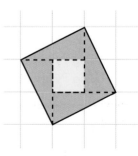

A ACTIVITY 1

a) Use either method 1 or method 2 to calculate the area of the squares in the diagram opposite.

b) Draw some more tilted squares of your own on squared paper and find their areas.

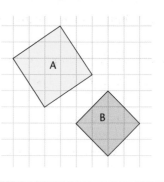

Look at all the tilted squares you draw in Activity 1.

Code the tilt by drawing a triangle at the base and writing down the length of its sides, like this.

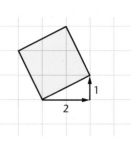

In this diagram the code is (2, 1). In the diagram in Activity 1, square A has a code of (3, 2) and square B has a code of (2, 2).

Check that you agree.

STAGE

7

Code all the squares you have drawn and write the codes and the areas of the squares in a table. Include the square from the beginning of this chapter. Its code is $(2, 0)$ and its area is 4 square units. Include all the other squares you have already studied in this chapter.

Look at the codes and their areas. See if you can find a rule linking them together.

Code	Area
$(2, 0)$	4
$(2, 1)$	5
$(3, 2)$	13
$(2, 2)$	8

You will have found that squaring each code number and then adding the squares together gives the area.

$2^2 + 0^2 = 4 + 0 = 4$
$2^2 + 1^2 = 4 + 1 = 5$
$3^2 + 2^2 = 9 + 4 = 13$
$2^2 + 2^2 = 4 + 4 = 8$

The rule linking them together is called **Pythagoras' theorem**.

> **Squaring the numbers in the code and adding them is the same as squaring the lengths of the sides of the triangle.**

Here is square A again.

Can you see that you can calculate the area of the largest square by adding together the areas of the smaller squares?

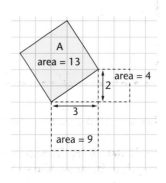

The largest square will always be on the longest side of the triangle – this is called the **hypotenuse** of the right-angled triangle.

Pythagoras' theorem can be stated like this.

> **The area of the square on the hypotenuse = the sum of the areas of the squares on the other two sides.**

Here is a shorter version.

> **The square on the hypotenuse = the sum of the squares on the other two sides.**

A ACTIVITY 2

Copy this diagram.

Cut up the two smaller squares so that they fit together to make square A.

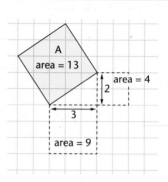

EXERCISE 10.1

Calculate the missing area in each of these diagrams.

1

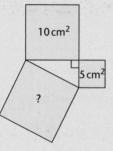

10 cm²

5 cm²

?

4

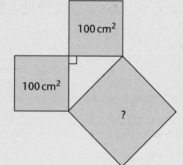

100 cm²

100 cm²

?

2

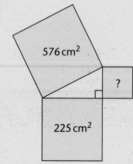

576 cm²

?

225 cm²

5

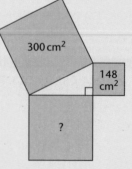

300 cm²

148 cm²

?

3

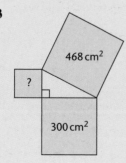

468 cm²

?

300 cm²

If you know the lengths of two sides of a right-angled triangle you can use Pythagoras' theorem to find the length of the third side.

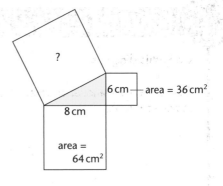

The unknown area = 64 + 36 = 100 cm²

This means that the sides of the unknown square have a length of $\sqrt{100} = 10$ cm.

When using Pythagoras' theorem, you don't need to draw the squares – you can simply use the rule.

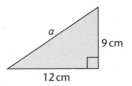

$$a^2 = b^2 + c^2$$

EXAMPLE 1

Find the length a in the diagram.

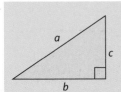

$a^2 = 9^2 + 12^2$
$\quad = 81 + 144$
$\quad = 225$
$a = \sqrt{225}$
$\quad = 15$ cm

EXAMPLE 2

Find the length a in the diagram.

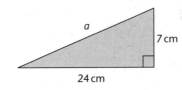

$a^2 = 7^2 + 24^2$
$\quad = 49 + 576$
$\quad = 625$
$a = \sqrt{625}$
$\quad = 25$ cm

STAGE

7

EXERCISE 10.2

Find the length of the hypotenuse, a, in each of these triangles.

1

a 4 cm
3 cm

4

a 8 cm
8 cm

2

5 cm a
10 cm

5
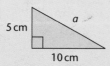
7 cm a
9 cm

3

2 cm
a 5 cm

6

5 cm
12 cm a

If you know the length of the hypotenuse and the length of one other side, you can find the length of the third side.

EXAMPLE 3

Find the length c in the diagram.

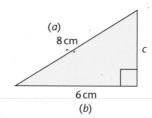

(a)
8 cm
c
6 cm
(b)

$a^2 = b^2 + c^2$
$8^2 = 6^2 + c^2$
$64 = 36 + c^2$
$c^2 = 64 - 36 = 28$
$c = \sqrt{28} = 5 \cdot 29 \, \text{cm}$ (to 2 decimal places)

EXERCISE 10.3

Calculate the length of the third side in each of the triangles in questions **1** to **8**.

Give your answers either exactly or correct to 2 decimal places.

1
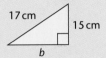

2

3

4

5

6

7

8
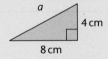

For each of the triangles in questions **9** to **17**, find the length marked *x*.

Give your answers either exactly or correct to 2 decimal places.

9
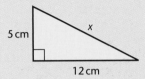

10
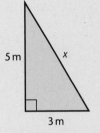

11
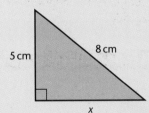

12
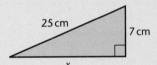

13
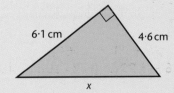

14
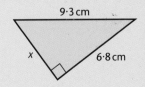

EXERCISE 10.3 continued

15

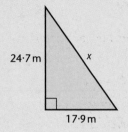

24·7 m   *x*

17·9 m

16

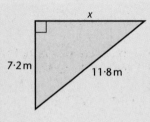

x

7·2 m

11·8 m

17

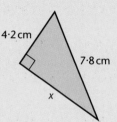

4·2 cm

7·8 cm

x

You can use Pythagoras' theorem to solve problems. It is a good idea to draw a sketch if a diagram isn't given. Try to draw it roughly to scale and mark on it any lengths you know.

EXAMPLE 4

Tom is standing 115 m from a vertical tower.

The tower is 20 m tall.

Work out the distance from Tom directly to the top of the tower.

$x^2 = 115^2 + 20^2$
$\quad = 13\,625$
$x = \sqrt{13\,625}$
$\quad = 116\cdot7\,m$ (to 1 decimal place)

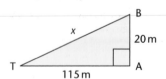

B
x
20 m
T
115 m
A

EXERCISE 10.4

Solve these problems. In each case draw a diagram first to help you.

1 A rectangular field is 225 m long and 110 m wide.
Find the length of the diagonal path across it.

2 A rectangular field is 25 m long.
A footpath 38·0 m long crosses the field diagonally.
Find the width of the field.

3 A ladder is 7 m long.
It is resting against a wall, with the top of the ladder 5 m above the ground.
How far from the wall is the base of the ladder?

4 Harry is making a kite for his sister.
This is his diagram of the kite.

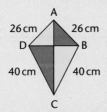

The kite is 30 cm wide.
Harry needs to buy some cane to make the struts AC and DB.
What length of cane does he need to buy?

5 This is the side view of a shed.

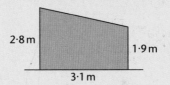

Find the length of the sloping roof.

6 This is the cross-section of a roof space.
The roof timbers AB and BC are each 6·5 m long.
The floor joist AC is 12 m.

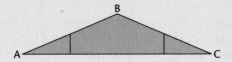

What is the maximum height in the roof space?

7 A tent pole is secured by guy ropes which are 2·4 m long.
They reach the ground, which is horizontal, 1·6 m away from the base of the pole.
How high up the pole are the guy ropes fastened?

Pythagorean triples

Look at these triangles.

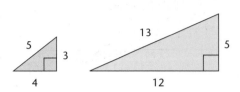
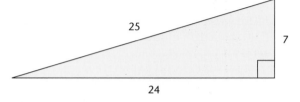

$$3^2 + 4^2 = 5^2 \qquad 5^2 + 12^2 = 13^2 \qquad 7^2 + 24^2 = 25^2$$

These are examples of **Pythagorean triples**, three numbers that exactly fit Pythagoras' relationship.

3, 4, 5   5, 12, 13   and   7, 24, 25   are the most well-known whole-number Pythagorean triples.

 ACTIVITY 3

Check that 2·5, 6, 6·5 is also a Pythagorean triple.

You can also use Pythagoras' theorem in reverse.

If the lengths of the three sides of a triangle form a Pythagorean triple, then the triangle is right-angled.

EXERCISE 10.5

State whether or not each of these triangles is right-angled. Show your working.

1
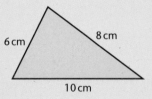

3
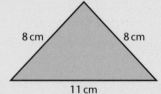

2
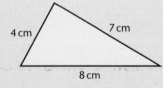

4
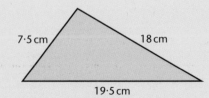

EXERCISE 10.5 continued

5

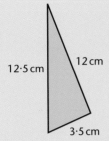
12·5 cm
12 cm
3·5 cm

7

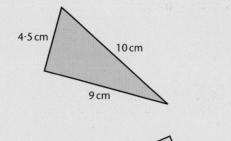
4·5 cm
10 cm
9 cm

6

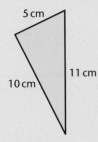
5 cm
11 cm
10 cm

8

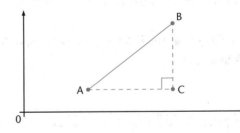
28·8 cm
12 cm
31·2 cm

C CHALLENGE 1

Plot the points A(3, 1) and B(7, 4) on squared paper.

Complete the right-angled triangle ABC.

Find the length of AB.

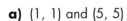

$AB^2 = AC^2 + BC^2$
$AC = 7 - 3 = 4$ and $BC = 4 - 1 = 3$
$AB^2 = 4^2 + 3^2 = 25$
$AB = 5$

Now find the distance between each of these pairs of points.

a) (1, 1) and (5, 5)

b) (6, 2) and (2, 1)

c) (3, 4) and (0, 0)

d) (−2, −1) and (4, 1)

STAGE

7

Pythagoras' theorem

K KEY IDEAS

- For a right-angled triangle, Pythagoras' theorem states that $a^2 = b^2 + c^2$.

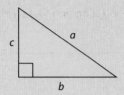

- A Pythagorean triple is a set of three numbers that exactly fits Pythagoras' relationship.

- If the lengths of the three sides of a triangle form a Pythagorean triple, then the triangle is right-angled.

STAGE

7

Revision exercise B1

1 Work out the size of each angle marked with a letter.
Give a reason for each of your answers.

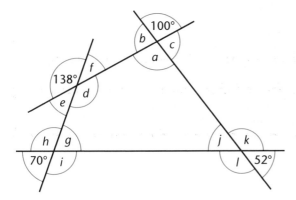

2 Work out the size of each angle marked with a letter.
Give a reason for each of your answers.

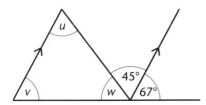

3 Four of the exterior angles of a pentagon are 85°, 66°, 54° and 97°.
Find the size of the other exterior angle.

4 Calculate the sum of the interior angles of a heptagon.

5 A regular polygon has ten sides.
Find the size of each of its exterior and interior angles.

6 An irregular polygon has eight sides.
Seven of its interior angles add up to 940°.
Calculate the size of its other interior angle.

7 Find the size of each angle marked with a letter.

a)

b)

c)

8 Calculate the size of the interior angle of a regular polygon with 20 sides.

9 Calculate the number of sides of a regular polygon with an interior angle of 168°.

10 £C is the cost of L m of piping.
C is directly proportional to L.
a) Copy and complete the table.

L	1·3	5·2	
C	3·12		6·00

b) State the equation connecting C and L.

11 Find the equation connecting y and x if y is directly proportional to x and y = 10·8 when x = 6.

STAG
7

12 A is directly proportional to h.
A = 5·6 when h = 4.
Calculate the value of A when h = 5.

13 Estimate the cost of travelling 48 miles by car if the cost per mile is 31p.

14 Stephen has £25.
Show a rough calculation to check whether he has enough money to buy six CDs at £3·98 each.

15 Estimate the answers to these.
   a) 63·9 × 14·9
   b) $\sqrt{143} \times \sqrt{170} \times \sqrt{80}$
   c) $(6·32 + 5·72) \times (\sqrt{16·1} + \sqrt{48·9})$

16 The scatter diagram shows the heights and weights of ten boys and ten girls in a class.

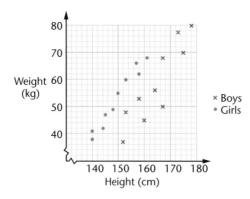

Weight (kg) / Height (cm)
× Boys
• Girls

Compare the boys and girls, noting any differences and any similarities.

17 Two judges at a cat show marked eight cats for the quality of their coats.
The marks are out of 30. The marks they gave are shown in the table.

Cat	Judge 1	Judge 2
A	17	7
B	23	23
C	15	9
D	28	27
E	22	13
F	18	15
G	27	25
H	14	4

   a) Draw a scatter diagram to show the judges' scores, with Judge 1 on the horizontal axis.
   b) Comment on the relationship between the two judges' scores.
   c) Draw a line of best fit.
   d) Judge 2 gave a ninth cat 18 marks. Estimate the marks that Judge 1 would give the same cat.

18 The table shows the predicted sales of replica shirts at different prices.

Price (£)	Number of shirts
20	7600
25	7400
30	6800
35	5600
40	5400
45	4500
50	3600

   a) Draw a scatter diagram to show this information.
   b) Comment on the relationship between price and predicted sales.
   c) Draw a line of best fit.
   d) Estimate the sales of shirts if the price is set at £33.
   e) Why would it be wrong to predict the sales of shirts priced at £65?

19 Calculate the value of x in each of these triangles.

   a)   b)
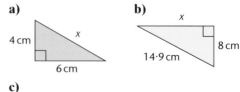

   c)

20 Calculate the length of the diagonal of a rectangle with length 22 cm and width 12 cm.

21 A ship sails 20 km due north and then 30 km due west.
How far is it from its starting point?

22 A triangle has sides of length 8 cm, 9 cm and 12 cm.
Use Pythagoras' theorem to check whether or not this is a right-angled triangle.

STAG
7

11 Quadratic graphs

You will learn about

- The shape of a quadratic graph
- Drawing a quadratic graph, given its equation
- Using a quadratic graph to solve equations

You should already know

- How to draw the graph of a straight line, given its equation

Drawing quadratic graphs

Quadratic graphs are graphs of equations of the form

$$y = ax^2 + bx + c$$

where a, b and c are constants, and b and c may be zero. Examples are quadratic equations are $y = x^2 + 3$ and $y = x^2 - 4x + 3$. When the graph is drawn, it produces a curve called a **parabola**.

A ACTIVITY 1

State whether or not each of these is quadratic.

a) $y = x^2$

b) $y = x^2 + 5x - 4$

c) $y = \dfrac{5}{x}$

d) $y = x^2 - 3x$

e) $y = x^2 - 3$

f) $y = x^3 + 5x^2 - 2$

g) $y = x(x - 2)$

EXAMPLE 1

Draw the graph of $y = x^2 + 4$, for values of x from $^-3$ to 3.

First make a table of values.

x	-3	-2	-1	0	1	2	3
x^2	9	4	1	0	1	4	9
+ 4	4	4	4	4	4	4	4
$y = x^2 + 4$	13	8	5	4	5	8	13

EXAM TIP

In an exam you may need to complete a table of values to work out the points. Even if you are not given a table to complete, it is still best to use one.

Now label the axes. The values of x go from $^-3$ to 3 and the values of y go from 4 to 13. It is better to include 0 in the values of y, so let them go from 0 to 15.

EXAM TIP

Always include the x-axis even when the y-values are all positive.

On this graph, the scales used are 1 cm to 1 unit on the x-axis and 1 cm to 5 units on the y-axis.

Plot the points and join them with a smooth curve. Label the curve.

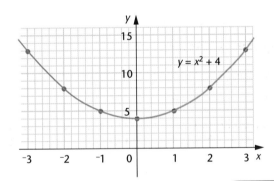

EXAM TIP

Practise drawing smooth curves. Keep your pencil on the paper. Make the curve a thin single line. Look ahead to the next point as you draw the line. It is easier with your hand inside the curve. Turn the page round if necessary.

EXAM TIP

x^2 is always positive so $-x^2$ is always negative. If the equation involves $-x^2$, the parabola will be the opposite way up. In quadratic graphs, the values of y go down and then up again (or the other way round). If one point does not fit the pattern, check that point again.

STAGE

7

EXAMPLE 2

Draw the graph of $y = x^2 + 3x$, for values of x from $^-5$ to 2.

First make a table of values.

x	−5	−4	−3	−2	−1	0	1	2
x²	25	16	9	4	1	0	1	4
+ 3x	−15	−12	−9	−6	−3	0	3	6
y = x² + 3x	10	4	0	−2	−2	0	4	10

Add the numbers in rows 2 and 3 to give each value of y.

Label the axes from $^-5$ to 2 for x and from $^-5$ to 10 for y.

EXAM TIP

A common error is to include the value in the x-row when adding to find y so separate this row off clearly.

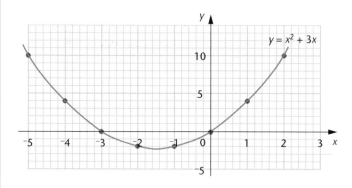

Here you can see that $x = ^-1$ and $x = ^-2$ both give $y = ^-2$, and the lowest value of y (called the **minimum**) will be when x is between $^-1$ and $^-2$.

It is useful to work out the value of y when $x = ^-1 \cdot 5$. To do this, add some more values to your table.

When $x = ^-1 \cdot 5$, $x^2 = 2 \cdot 25$ and $3x = ^-4 \cdot 5$, so $y = ^-2 \cdot 25$.

Plot $(^-1 \cdot 5, ^-2 \cdot 25)$, which is the lowest point of the graph.

EXAM TIP

The y-scale in Examples 1 and 2 is 1 cm to 5 units. This is satisfactory and does not take a lot of space, but if you do have enough space the graph will look better and be easier to plot if you use a scale of 2 cm to 5 units, as in Example 3.

EXAM TIP

If you find that you have two equal lowest (or highest) values for y, the curve will go below (or above) that value. You will need to find the y-value between the two equal values. To do this, find the value of x halfway between the two points and substitute to find the corresponding value of y.

EXAMPLE 3

a) Draw the graph of $y = x^2 - 2x - 3$, for values of x from $^-2$ to 4.

Label the axes from $^-2$ to 4 for x, and from $^-5$ to 5 for y.

b) Find the values of x for which $y = 0$.

a)

x	-2	-1	0	1	2	3	4
x^2	4	1	0	1	4	9	16
- 2x	4	2	0	-2	-4	-6	-8
- 3	-3	-3	-3	-3	-3	-3	-3
y = x^2 – 2x – 3	5	0	-3	-4	-3	0	5

> **EXAM TIP**
>
> Sometimes a table will be given with only the two rows for the x- and y-values.
>
> You may find it useful to include all the rows and then just add the correct rows to get the values of y.

To find the value of y, add together the values in rows 2, 3 and 4.

Use a scale of 1 cm to 1 unit on the x-axis and 2 squares to 5 units on the y-axis. Now plot the points $(^-2, 5)$, $(^-1, 0)$, and so on. Join them with a smooth curve. Label the curve.

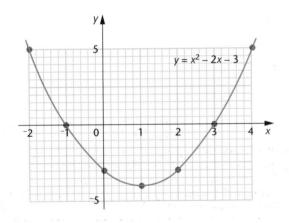

b) $y = 0$ when the curve crosses the x-axis.
This is when $x = ^-1$ or $x = 3$.

Sometimes questions will be put in context. They will be about a real-life situation, rather than just being about a graph in terms of x and y.

EXAMPLE 4

The cost C, in pounds, of circular plates is given by the formula $C = \dfrac{x^2}{10} + 2$, where x is the radius of the plate in centimetres.

a) Draw up a table of values and complete it.

b) (i) Draw the graph of C against x, for values of x from 5 to 20.
(ii) From your graph find the size of plate that would cost £16·40.

a)

x	5	8	10	15	20
$\dfrac{x^2}{10}$	2·5	6·4	10	22·5	40
+ 2	2	2	2	2	2
$C = \dfrac{x^2}{10} + 2$	4·5	8·4	12	24·5	42

> **EXAM TIP**
> Always draw your curve in pencil so you can rub out any errors.

b) (i)

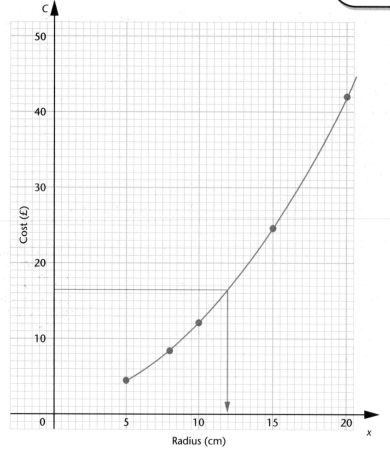

(ii) You can buy a plate with radius 12 cm for £16·40.

EXERCISE 11.1

1 Copy and complete this table for $y = x^2 + 5$. Do not draw the graph.

x	-3	-2	-1	0	1	2	3
x^2	9						
+ 5	5						
$y = x^2 + 5$	14						

2 Copy and complete this table for $y = x^2 + 6$. Do not draw the graph.

x	-3	-2	-1	0	1	2	3
x^2		4					
+ 6		6					
$y = x^2 + 6$		10					

3 Copy and complete this table for $y = x^2 + 3x - 7$. Do not draw the graph.
Notice the extra value at $x = {}^-1 \cdot 5$.

x	-4	-3	-2	-1	0	1	2	-1·5
x^2			4					
+ 3x			-6					
- 7			-7					
$y = x^2 + 3x - 7$			-9					

4 Copy and complete this table for $y = 2x^2 - 8$. Do not draw the graph.

x	-3	-2	-1	0	1	2	3
x^2	9						
$2x^2$	18						
- 8	-8						
$y = 2x^2 - 8$	10						

Hint: To find the value of y, rows 3 and 4 are added. Some people do not include the x^2 row but it can help.

STAGE

7

EXERCISE 11.1 continued

5 Copy and complete this table for $y = {}^-x^2 - 5x + 6$. Do not draw the graph.
Remember that ${}^-x^2$ is always negative. Notice the extra value at ${}^-2{\cdot}5$.

x	⁻6	⁻5	⁻4	⁻3	⁻2	⁻1	0	1	2	⁻2·5
⁻x²		⁻16						⁻4		
– 5x			20						⁻10	
+ 6			6						6	
y = ⁻x² – 5x + 6			10						⁻8	

6 Make a table of values for $y = x^2 - 3x + 1$, for values of x from ⁻2 to 4.
Do not draw the graph.

7 Make a table of values for $y = x^2 - 5x + 8$, for values of x from ⁻2 to 4.
Do not draw the graph.

Use 2 mm graph paper for questions **8** to **20**.

8 **a)** Copy and complete this table for $y = x^2 - 2$.

x	⁻3	⁻2	⁻1	0	1	2	3
x²							
– 2							
y = x² – 2							

b) Draw the graph of $y = x^2 - 2$, for values of x from ⁻3 to 3.
Label the x-axis from ⁻3 to 3 and the y-axis from ⁻5 to 10.
Use a scale of 1 cm to 1 unit on the x-axis and 2 cm to 5 units on the y-axis.

9 **a)** Copy and complete this table for $y = x^2 - 3x$.

x	⁻1	0	1	2	3	4	5	1·5
x²								
– 3x								
y = x² – 3x								

b) Draw the graph of $y = x^2 - 3x$, for values of x from ⁻1 to 5.
Label the x-axis from ⁻1 to 5 and the y-axis from ⁻5 to 10.
Use a scale of 1 cm to 1 unit on the x-axis and 2 cm to 5 units on the y-axis.

10 Draw the graph of $y = {}^-x^2 + 4$, for values of x from ⁻3 to 3.
Label the x-axis from ⁻3 to 3 and the y-axis from ⁻5 to 5.
Use a scale of 1 cm to 1 unit on the x-axis and 2 cm to 5 units on the y-axis.

11 Draw the graph of $y = x^2 + 4x$, for values of x from $^-6$ to 2.
Label the x-axis from $^-6$ to 2 and the y-axis from $^-5$ to 15.
Use a scale of 1 cm to 1 unit on the x-axis and 1 cm to 5 units on the y-axis.

12 Draw the graph of $y = {}^-x^2 + 2x + 6$, for values of x from $^-2$ to 4.
Label the x-axis from $^-2$ to 4 and the y-axis from $^-5$ to 10.
Use a scale of 1 cm to 1 unit on the x-axis and 1 cm to
5 units on the y-axis.

13 Draw the graph of $y = x^2 - 4x + 3$, for values of x from $^-1$ to 5.

14 Draw the graph of $y = x^2 - 6x + 5$, for values of x from $^-1$ to 6.

15 Draw the graph of $y = {}^-x^2 + 4x - 3$, for values of x from $^-1$ to 5.

16 a) Draw the graph of $y = x^2 - 5x + 2$, for values of
x from $^-1$ to 6.
    b) Find the values of x on your graph when $y = 0$.
Give your answers correct to 1 decimal place.

Hint:
An extra point at $x = 2.5$ might be useful.

17 a) Draw the graph of $y = 2x^2 - 5x + 1$, for values
of x from $^-2$ to 4.
    b) Find the value of x on your graph where $y = 0$.
Give your answers correct to 1 decimal place.

Hint:
Note that in this case the values of y are not symmetrical.

18 a) Draw the graph of $y = 2x^2 - 12x$, for values of x from $^-1$ to 7.
    b) Write down the values of x where the curve crosses $y = 5$.

19 When a stone is dropped from the edge of a cliff, the distance, d metres, it falls is
given by the formula $d = 5t^2$, where t is the time in seconds.
    a) Work out the values of d for values of t from 0 to 5.
    b) Draw the graph for $t = 0$ to 5.
    c) The cliff is 65 metres high.
How long does it take the stone to reach the bottom of the cliff?
Give your answer correct to 1 decimal place.

20 The surface area of a cube (S) is given by the formula $S = 6x^2$, where x is the length
of an edge of the cube.
    a) Copy this table of values and complete it to find S.

x	0	1	2	3	4	5	6
x²				9			
S = 6x²				54			

    b) Draw the graph of $S = 6x^2$ for values of x from 0 to 6.
    c) From your graph, find the length of the edge of a cube with surface area 140 cm².

Graphical methods of solving equations

One way of finding solutions to quadratic equations is to draw and use a graph.

EXAMPLE 5

a) Draw the graph of $y = x^2 - 2x - 8$, for values of x from $^-3$ to 5.

b) Solve the equation $x^2 - 2x - 8 = 0$.

c) Solve the equation $x^2 - 2x - 8 = 5$.

a)

x	-3	-2	-1	0	1	2	3	4	5
x^2	9	4	1	0	1	4	9	16	25
$- 2x$	6	4	2	0	-2	-4	-6	-8	-10
$- 8$	-8	-8	-8	-8	-8	-8	-8	-8	-8
$y = x^2 - 2x - 8$	7	0	-5	-8	-9	-8	-5	0	7

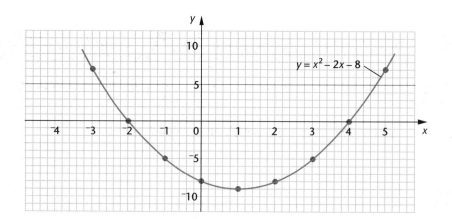

b) The solution of $x^2 - 2x - 8 = 0$ is when $y = 0$, where the curve cuts the x-axis.
The solution is $x = ^-2$ or $x = 4$.

c) The solution of $x^2 - 2x - 8 = 5$ is when $y = 5$.
Draw the line $y = 5$ on your graph and read off the values of x where the curve cuts the line.
The solution is $x = ^-2 \cdot 7$ or $x = 4 \cdot 7$, to 1 decimal place.

EXERCISE 11.2

1 a) Draw the graph of $y = x^2 - 7x + 10$, for values of x from 0 to 7.

b) Solve the equation $x^2 - 7x + 10 = 0$.

2 a) Draw the graph of $y = x^2 - x - 2$, for values of x from $^-2$ to 3.

b) Solve the equation $x^2 - x - 2 = 0$.

3 a) Draw the graph of $y = x^2 - 8$, for values of x from $^-4$ to 4.

b) Solve the equation $x^2 - 8 = 0$.

c) Solve the equation $x^2 - 8 = 3$.

4 a) Draw the graph of $y = x^2 + x - 3$, for values of x from $^-3$ to 2.

b) Solve the equation $x^2 + x - 3 = 0$.

c) Solve the equation $x^2 + x - 3 = ^-2$.

5 a) Draw the graph of $y = x^2 - 4x + 3$, for values of x from $^-1$ to 5.

b) Solve the equation $x^2 - 4x + 3 = 0$.

6 a) Draw the graph of $y = x^2 - 3x$, for values of x from $^-2$ to 5.

b) Solve the equation $x^2 - 3x = 0$.

7 a) Draw the graph of $y = x^2 - 5$, for values of x from $^-3$ to 3.

b) Solve the equation $x^2 - 5 = 0$.

c) Solve the equation $x^2 - 5 = 2$.

8 a) Draw the graph of $y = x^2 - 3x - 2$, for values of x from $^-2$ to 5.

b) Solve the equation $x^2 - 3x - 2 = 0$.

c) Solve the equation $x^2 - 3x - 2 = 6$.

K KEY IDEAS

■ Quadratic equations have the form $y = ax^2 + bx + c$, where a, b and c are constants, and b and c may be zero.

■ The graph of a quadratic equation is a parabola. It has this shape.

if $a > 0$ if $a < 0$

■ To solve the quadratic equation $ax^2 + bx + c = k$ graphically, find the values of x where the graph of $y = ax^2 + bx + c$ crosses the line $y = k$.

STAGE

7

12 Finding the mean of grouped data

Finding the mean of grouped discrete data

When working out the mean of grouped data in a table, you do not know the exact value for each item of data, so the midpoint value is chosen to represent each group, and this is used to calculate an **estimate** of the mean. The midpoint value is multiplied by the frequency of the group.

One method for finding the midpoint of a group is to add the end values of the group and divide by 2. For example, if the group is $60 \leqslant s < 80$, then the midpoint is $\dfrac{60 + 80}{2} = 70$.

EXAMPLE 1

The table shows the scores of 40 students in a history test.

Score (s)	Frequency
$0 \leqslant s < 20$	2
$20 \leqslant s < 40$	4
$40 \leqslant s < 60$	14
$60 \leqslant s < 80$	16
$80 \leqslant s < 100$	4
Total	40

EXAM TIP
Add two columns to the frequency table to help you work out the mean: one column for the midpoint of each group and one for the midpoint multiplied by the frequency of the group.

Calculate an estimate of the mean score.

Score (s)	Frequency	Midpoint	Midpoint × frequency
$0 \leqslant s < 20$	2	10	20
$20 \leqslant s < 40$	4	30	120
$40 \leqslant s < 60$	14	50	700
$60 \leqslant s < 80$	16	70	1120
$80 \leqslant s < 100$	4	90	360
Total	40		2320

Mean = 2320 ÷ 40 = 58

EXAM TIP
Don't forget to divide by the total frequency, not the number of groups.

EXERCISE 12.1

1 The table shows a summary of the marks scored by students in a test. Calculate an estimate of the mean score for these students.

Marks (m)	Frequency
$0 \leqslant m < 20$	1
$20 \leqslant m < 40$	3
$40 \leqslant m < 60$	15
$60 \leqslant m < 80$	9
$80 \leqslant m < 100$	2

2 The table summarises the number of words in each sentence on one page of a book. Calculate the mean length of a sentence.

Number of words	Frequency
1–3	0
4–6	2
7–9	7
10–12	6
13–15	15

STAGE

7

3 The table shows a summary of the attendance at the first 30 games of a football club.
Calculate an estimate of the mean attendance.

Attendance (a)	Frequency
$0 \leqslant a < 4000$	0
$4000 \leqslant a < 8000$	2
$8000 \leqslant a < 12\,000$	7
$12\,000 \leqslant a < 16\,000$	6
$16\,000 \leqslant a < 20\,000$	15

4 The table shows a summary of the number of points scored by a school basketball player.
Calculate an estimate of their mean points score.

Points (p)	Frequency
$0 \leqslant p < 5$	2
$5 \leqslant p < 10$	3
$10 \leqslant p < 15$	8
$15 \leqslant p < 20$	9
$20 \leqslant p < 25$	12
$25 \leqslant p < 30$	3

5 The number of road accidents in a small town was recorded each week over two years. The table summarises the information gathered.
Calculate an estimate of the mean number of accidents per week.

Number of accidents	Frequency
0–1	1
2–3	7
4–5	12
6–9	36
10–14	28
15–17	19
18–20	1

Finding the mean of grouped continuous data

You use the same method to calculate an estimate of the mean of grouped continuous data as for grouped discrete data.

▌ EXAMPLE 2

The table shows the heights of the students in Year 11 at Sandish School.

Height (h cm)	Frequency
$155 \leqslant h < 160$	2
$160 \leqslant h < 165$	6
$165 \leqslant h < 170$	18
$170 \leqslant h < 175$	25
$175 \leqslant h < 180$	9
$180 \leqslant h < 185$	4
$185 \leqslant h < 190$	1
Total	65

Calculate an estimate of the mean height.

Height (h cm)	Frequency	Midpoint	Midpoint × frequency
$155 \leqslant h < 160$	2	157·5	315
$160 \leqslant h < 165$	6	162·5	975
$165 \leqslant h < 170$	18	167·5	3 015
$170 \leqslant h < 175$	25	172·5	4 312·5
$175 \leqslant h < 180$	9	177·5	1 597·5
$180 \leqslant h < 185$	4	182·5	730
$185 \leqslant h < 190$	1	187·5	187·5
Total	65		11 132·5

Mean = 11 132·5 ÷ 65 = 171·3 cm, correct to 1 decimal place.

STAGE

7

A ACTIVITY 1

a) Collect some continuous data, for example the masses of school bags for people in your class.

b) Group the data and represent them on a frequency polygon or bar graph. Calculate the mean of the data.

EXERCISE 12.2

1 Calculate an estimate of the mean of these times.

Time (t seconds)	Frequency
$0 \leqslant t < 2$	4
$2 \leqslant t < 4$	6
$4 \leqslant t < 6$	3
$6 \leqslant t < 8$	2
$8 \leqslant t < 10$	7

2 Calculate an estimate of the mean of these heights.

Height (h cm)	Frequency
$50 \leqslant h < 60$	15
$60 \leqslant h < 70$	23
$70 \leqslant h < 80$	38
$80 \leqslant h < 90$	17
$90 \leqslant h < 100$	7

3 Calculate an estimate of the mean of these lengths.

Length (l metres)	Frequency
$1{\cdot}0 \leqslant l < 1{\cdot}2$	2
$1{\cdot}2 \leqslant l < 1{\cdot}4$	7
$1{\cdot}4 \leqslant l < 1{\cdot}6$	13
$1{\cdot}6 \leqslant l < 1{\cdot}8$	5
$1{\cdot}8 \leqslant l < 2{\cdot}0$	3

4 Calculate an estimate of the mean length for this distribution.

Length (y cm)	Frequency
$10 \leqslant y < 20$	2
$20 \leqslant y < 30$	6
$30 \leqslant y < 40$	9
$40 \leqslant y < 50$	5
$50 \leqslant y < 60$	3

5 Calculate an estimate of the mean mass of these tomatoes.

Mass of tomato (t g)	Frequency
$35 < t \leqslant 40$	7
$40 < t \leqslant 45$	13
$45 < t \leqslant 50$	20
$50 < t \leqslant 55$	16
$55 < t \leqslant 60$	4

6 Calculate an estimate of the mean of these times.

Time (t seconds)	Frequency
$0 \leqslant t < 20$	4
$20 \leqslant t < 40$	9
$40 \leqslant t < 60$	13
$60 \leqslant t < 80$	8
$80 \leqslant t < 100$	6

EXERCISE 12.2 continued

7 Calculate an estimate of the mean of these heights.

Height (h metres)	Frequency
$0 < h \leqslant 2$	12
$2 < h \leqslant 4$	26
$4 < h \leqslant 6$	34
$6 < h \leqslant 8$	23
$8 < h \leqslant 10$	5

8 Calculate an estimate of the mean of these lengths.

Length (l cm)	Frequency
$3 \cdot 0 \leqslant l < 3 \cdot 2$	3
$3 \cdot 2 \leqslant l < 3 \cdot 4$	8
$3 \cdot 4 \leqslant l < 3 \cdot 6$	11
$3 \cdot 6 \leqslant l < 3 \cdot 8$	5
$3 \cdot 8 \leqslant l < 4 \cdot 0$	3

9 Calculate an estimate of the mean of these masses.

Mass (w kg)	Frequency
$30 \leqslant w < 40$	5
$40 \leqslant w < 50$	8
$50 \leqslant w < 60$	2
$60 \leqslant w < 70$	4
$70 \leqslant w < 80$	1

10 Calculate an estimate of the mean of these lengths.

Length (x cm)	Frequency
$0 < x \leqslant 5$	8
$5 < x \leqslant 10$	6
$10 < x \leqslant 15$	2
$15 < x \leqslant 20$	5
$20 < x \leqslant 25$	1

C CHALLENGE 1

The bar graph shows the masses of a sample of 50 eggs.

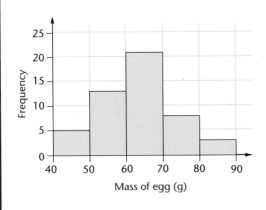

a) Make a frequency table for this information.

b) Calculate an estimate of the mean mass of these eggs.

STAGE
7

C CHALLENGE 2

The bar graph shows the heights of students in Year 9.

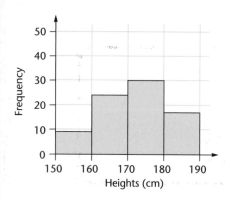

a) Make a frequency table for this information.

b) Calculate an estimate of the mean height.

K KEY IDEAS

- To find an estimate of the mean of grouped data, use the midpoint of each group as the value for the group, multiply each value by the group frequency, add the results and divide by the sum of their frequencies.

Equations and inequalities 1

You will learn about

- The meaning of the four inequality symbols
- Solving linear inequalities
- Showing the solution to an inequality on a number line
- Forming and solving linear equations and inequalities

You should already know

- How to write a simple formula in letters
- How to collect together simple algebraic terms
- How to multiply out expressions such as $3(2x - 5)$
- How to solve linear equations

Inequalities

$a < b$ means 'a is less than b'

$a \leqslant b$ means 'a is less than or equal to b'

$a > b$ means 'a is greater than b'

$a \geqslant b$ means 'a is greater than or equal to b'

Expressions involving these signs are called *inequalities*.

STAGE
7

EXAMPLE 1

Find the integer (whole number) values of x for each of these inequalities.

a) $^-3 < x \leqslant {}^-1$ **b)** $1 \leqslant x < 4$

a) If $^-3 < x \leqslant {}^-1$, then $x = {}^-2$ or $^-1$.   Note that $^-3$ is not included but $^-1$ is.

b) If $1 \leqslant x < 4$, then $x = 1, 2$ or 3.   Note that 1 is included but 4 is not.

In equations, if you always do the same thing to both sides the equality is still valid. The same is *usually* true for inequalities, but there is one important exception.

Consider the inequality $5 < 7$.

Add 2 to each side:	$7 < 9$	Still true
Subtract 5 from each side:	$2 < 4$	Still true
Multiply each side by 3:	$6 < 12$	Still true
Divide each side by 2:	$3 < 6$	Still true
Multiply each side by $^-2$:	$^-6 < ^-12$	No longer true
But reverse the inequality sign:	$^-6 > ^-12$	Now true

> **If you multiply or divide an inequality by a negative number, you must reverse the inequality sign.**

Otherwise inequalities can be treated in the same way as equations.

EXAMPLE 2

Solve each of these inequalities and show the solution on a number line.

a) $3x + 4 < 10$ **b)** $2x - 5 \leqslant 4 - 3x$ **c)** $x + 4 < 3x - 2$

a) $3x + 4 < 10$
     $3x < 6$ Subtract 4 from each side.
       $x < 2$ Divide each side by 2.

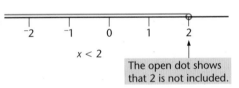

The open dot shows that 2 is not included.

b) $2x - 5 \leqslant 4 - 3x$
     $2x \leqslant 9 - 3x$ Add 5 to each side.
     $5x \leqslant 9$ Add 3x to each side.
       $x \leqslant 1{\cdot}8$ Divide each side by 5.

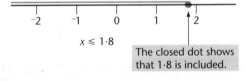

The closed dot shows that 1·8 is included.

c) $x + 4 < 3x - 2$
       $x < 3x - 6$ Subtract 4 from each side.
    $^-2x < ^-6$ Subtract 3x from each side.
       $x > 3$ Divide each side by $^-2$ and change $<$ to $>$ (when dividing by $^-2$).

You can avoid dealing with negative numbers by using an alternative method.

     $x + 4 < 3x - 2$
     $x + 6 < 3x$ Add 2 to each side.
       $6 < 2x$ Subtract x from each side.
       $3 < x$ Divide each side by 2.
       $x > 3$ Rewrite the inequality with x as the subject.

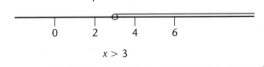

EXERCISE 13.1

1 Write down two possible values of x for the inequality $x < {}^-2$.

2 Write down the integer values of x for each of these inequalities.
  a) $^-4 \leqslant x < 0$
  b) $1 < x \leqslant 5$
  c) $1 < x \leqslant 4$
  d) $^-5 < x \leqslant {}^-1$

Solve the inequalities in questions **3** to **24**. For questions **3** to **10**, represent your solution on a number line.

3 $x - 3 \leqslant 4$

4 $x + 7 > 9$

5 $2x - 3 < 5$

6 $3x + 4 \leqslant 7$

7 $x - 2 < 5$

8 $2x + 3 > 6$

9 $3x - 4 \leqslant 8$

10 $3x \geqslant x - 2$

11 $2x \geqslant x + 5$

12 $5x > 3 - x$

13 $2x + 1 < 7$

14 $4x > 2x + 5$

15 $3x - 6 \geqslant x + 2$

16 $4x + 2 < 3$

17 $5a - 3 > 2a$

18 $2x - 3 < x + 1$

19 $3x + 2 \geqslant x - 1$

20 $3x + 7 < x + 3$

21 $8x - 10 > 3x + 25$

22 $2x - 7 \geqslant 5x + 8$

23 $6x + 11 \leqslant 18 - x$

24 $2x + 9 > 4x + 5$

C CHALLENGE 1

Given that x is an integer, solve each of these inequalities.

a) $3 \leqslant 2x - 1 \leqslant 5$

b) $^-4 \leqslant 3x + 2 \leqslant 11$

STAGE
7

Forming equations and inequalities

Everyday problems can often be solved by forming equations or inequalities and solving them.

EXAMPLE 3

The length of a rectangle is 4 cm greater than its width, which is x cm.

a) Write down an expression in terms of x for the perimeter of the rectangle.

b) The perimeter is 32 cm. Write down an equation in x and solve it.

c) What are the length and the width of the rectangle?

a) The length is 4 cm greater than the width, so the length is $(x + 4)$ cm.
Perimeter $= x + x + 4 + x + x + 4 = 4x + 8$

b) The perimeter is 32 cm, so

$$4x + 8 = 32$$
$$4x = 24$$
$$x = 6$$

c) The width is x cm $= 6$ cm.
The length is $(x + 4)$ cm $= 10$ cm.

EXAMPLE 4

John is having a party but he has only £60 to spend on it.
He has to pay £10 to hire the room and £4 for every person at the party.

How many people can he invite to his party?

Let the number of people be n.
Write down an inequality involving n and solve it to find the largest number that can go to the party.

Cost of party $\leqslant$ £60
So $10 + 4n \leqslant 60$
$$4n \leqslant 50$$
$$n \leqslant 12 \cdot 5$$

So the largest number of people that can go to the party is 12.

STAGE
7

> **EXAM TIP**
> Always think whether an answer is sensible. In this example, the final answer must be a whole number!

EXERCISE 13.2

1 Erica is x years old and Jayne is three years older than Erica. Their ages add up to 23.
Write down an equation in x and solve it to find their ages.

2 Two angles of a triangle are the same and the other is 15° bigger. Call the two equal angles a.
Write down an equation and solve it to find all the angles.

3 A man is wallpapering a room. It takes him 30 minutes to prepare his paste and 20 minutes to cut and hang each length of paper. He works for 4 hours and hangs x lengths.

Write down an inequality in x and solve it to find the largest number of lengths he can hang in the time.

4 In Devonshire School there are 28 more girls than boys. There are 616 students in the school altogether.
   a) Let the number of boys be x. Write down an equation in x and solve it.
   b) How many boys and how many girls are in the school?

5 To hire a bus, the charge is £60 plus £2 a mile. The bus company will only hire the bus if they take at least £225.
   a) Let the number of miles be x. Write down an inequality for x and solve it.
   b) What is the smallest distance that the bus can be hired to go?

6 It costs £x to hire a bike for an adult, and it is £2 cheaper for a child's bike. Mr Newton hires bikes for two adults and three children.

   a) Write down an expression in x for the cost of the bikes.
   b) The cost is £19. Write down an equation and solve it to find x.
   c) How much did each bike cost?

7 Ameer has 40 metres of fencing, in 1 metre lengths that cannot be split. He wants to use as much of it as he can to enclose a rectangle that is twice as long as it is wide.
   a) Call the width of the rectangle x metres and write down an inequality.
   b) Solve it to find the length and width of the biggest rectangle that he can make.

8 Mark, Patrick and Iain all collect toy cars. Mark has four more than Patrick, and Iain has three more than Mark. They have 41 cars altogether.
Set up an equation and solve it to find how many toy cars each boy has.

9 Mrs Pippard and her daughter go shopping. Mrs Pippard spends £x and her daughter spends twice as much. They spend £45 altogether.
Set up an equation and solve it to find how much each spends.

EXAM TIP
In these questions you can sometimes work out the answer without writing down the equation or inequality. But you must write it down when asked to in an examination, otherwise you will lose marks.

10 A pentagon has two angles of 150°, two of $x°$ and one of $(x + 30)°$. The sum of the angles in a pentagon is 540°.

a) Write down an equation in x and solve it.

b) State the size of each of the angles.

11 Sara is x years old, and Mary is ten years older than Sara. The sum of their ages is less than 50.

a) Write down an inequality and solve it.

b) What is the oldest that Sara can be?

12 On a school trip to France, there are 15 more girls than boys. Altogether 53 students go on the trip.

a) If the number of boys is x, write down an equation in x and solve it.

b) How many boys and how many girls go on the trip?

13 Paul goes to a shop and buys two chocolate bars at 30p each and x cans of cola at 45p each. He has £2 and wants to buy as many cans of cola as possible.

a) Write down an inequality in x and solve it.

b) What is the largest number of cans of cola he can buy?

14 At a café a cup of tea costs x pence, and a cup of coffee costs 10p more than a cup of tea. David spends £1·20 on three teas and two coffees.

a) Write down an equation in x and solve it.

b) What do tea and coffee cost at the café?

15 A firm employs 140 people, of whom x are men. There are ten fewer women than men.
Use algebra to find how many men and how many women work for the firm.

16 It costs £5 for each person to go skating. Skates can be hired for £2. Ten friends went skating and n of them hired skates.

a) Write down an expression in pounds for the total amount they spent.

b) They spent £62. Write down an equation in n and solve it to find how many hired skates.

KEY IDEAS

- $a < b$ means 'a is less than b'.
  $a \leq b$ means 'a is less than or equal to b'.
  $a > b$ means 'a is greater than b'.
  $a \geq b$ means 'a is greater than or equal to b'.

- Inequalities can be treated like equations, except when multiplying or dividing by a negative number you must reverse the inequality sign.

- You can use algebra to solve a problem by setting up an equation or inequality for the unknown quantity and then solving it.

STAGE

7

14 Compound measures

Speed

Speed is a **compound measure** because it is calculated from two other measurements: distance and time.

$$\text{Average speed} = \frac{\text{total distance travelled}}{\text{total time taken}}$$

The units of your answer will depend on the units you begin with. Speed has units of 'distance per time', for example km/h.

The formula for speed can be rearranged to find the distance travelled or the time taken for a journey.

$$\text{Distance} = \text{speed} \times \text{time} \qquad \text{Time} = \frac{\text{distance}}{\text{speed}}$$

EXAM TIP
You may find the d.s.t. triangle helpful. Cover up the quantity you are trying to find.

EXAMPLE 1

Find the average speed of an athlete who runs 100 metres in 20 seconds.

Average speed $= \dfrac{100\,m}{20\,s} = 5\,m/s$

EXAMPLE 2

How many minutes does it take to walk 2 km at a speed of 5 km/h?

Time $= \dfrac{distance}{speed} = \dfrac{2}{5}$ hour $= \dfrac{2}{5} \times 60$ minutes $= 24$ minutes

EXAMPLE 3

Find the average speed of a delivery driver who travels 45 km in 30 minutes.

Average speed $= \dfrac{45\,km}{30\,minutes} = 1\cdot5$ km/minute

However, the speed here is more likely to be needed in kilometres per hour.
To find this, first change the time into hours.

30 minutes = 0·5 hour

Average speed $= \dfrac{45\,km}{0.5\,h} = 90\,km/h$

You may also be able to see other ways of obtaining the results in Examples 2 and 3.

A ACTIVITY 1

Discuss some everyday situations in which you use speeds. Use appropriate numbers and units.

STAGE
7

Density

Another example of a compound measure is density, which links mass and volume.

$$\text{Density of a substance} = \frac{\text{mass}}{\text{volume}}$$

It is measured in units such as grams per cubic centimetre (g/cm^3).

EXAM TIP

As with speed, there is a triangle that can be helpful with these questions.

mass

density × volume

EXAMPLE 4

The density of gold is $19.3\,\text{g/cm}^3$. Calculate the mass of a gold bar with a volume of $30\,\text{cm}^3$.

$$\text{Density} = \frac{\text{mass}}{\text{volume}}$$

so mass = density × volume.

The mass of the gold bar = density × volume = $19.3 \times 30 = 579\,\text{g}$.

GOLD

Population density

Population density is another example of a compound measure. It gives an idea of how heavily populated an area is. It is measured as the number of people per square kilometre.

EXAM TIP

Once again, a triangle can be helpful with these questions.

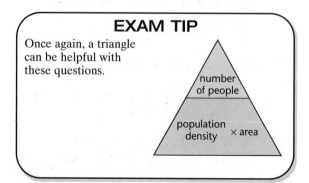

number of people

population density × area

EXAMPLE 5

In a small town, 300 people live in an area of 2.4 km². Find the population density of the town.

Population density $= \dfrac{300}{2 \cdot 4} = 125$ people/km²

EXERCISE 14.1

1 Find the average speed of a car which travels 75 miles in $1\frac{1}{2}$ hours.

2 Find the average speed of a runner who covers 180 m in 40 seconds.

3 Calculate the density of a stone of mass 350 g and volume 40 cm³.

4 Waring has a population of 60 000 in an area of 8 square kilometres. Calculate its population density.

5 A motorbike travels 1 mile in 3 minutes. Calculate its average speed in miles per hour.

6 Find the average speed of a car which travels 63 miles in $1\frac{1}{2}$ hours.

7 Find the average speed of a runner who covers 180 m in 48 seconds.

8 Calculate the density of a stone of mass 690 g and volume 74 cm³. Give your answer to a suitable degree of accuracy.

9 Trenton has a population of 65 000 in an area of 5·8 square kilometres. Calculate its population density, correct to the nearest thousand.

10 A cyclist rides 0·6 mile in 3 minutes. Calculate her average speed in miles per hour.

11 A bus travels at 5 m/s on average. How many kilometres per hour is this?

12 A foam plastic ball with volume 20 cm³ has density 0·3 g/cm³. What is its mass?

13 A town has a population of 200 000. Its population density is 10 000 people per square mile. What is the area of the town?

14 A runner's average speed in a 80 m race is 7 m/s. Find the time he takes for the race, to the nearest 0·1 second.

15 A car travels 15 km in 12 minutes. What is the average speed in km/h?

16 A bus travels at 6·1 m/s on average. How many kilometres per hour is this?

17 A rubber ball with volume 28·3 cm³ has density 0·7 g/cm³. What is its mass?

18 A town has a population of 276 300. Its population density is 9800 people per square mile. What is the area of the town?

19 A runner's average speed in a 200 m race is 5·3 m/s. Find the time she takes for the race, to the nearest 0·1 second.

20 A car travels 15 km in 14 minutes. What is the average speed in km/h?

STAGE 7

K KEY IDEAS

■ Average speed (measured in units such as m/s), density (measured in units such as g/cm^3) and population density (measured in units such as people/km^2) are compound measures.

■ Average speed = $\dfrac{\text{total distance travelled}}{\text{total time taken}}$

■ Density = $\dfrac{\text{mass}}{\text{volume}}$

■ Population density = $\dfrac{\text{number of people}}{\text{area}}$

STAGE
7

Reciprocals, factors and multiples

15

You will learn about

- Finding the reciprocal of a number
- Writing a number as a product of its prime factors
- Finding the highest common factor and lowest common multiple of two numbers

You should already know

- The meaning of the terms *reciprocal*, *factor* and *multiple*
- How to convert fractions to decimals

Reciprocals

You should already know that the reciprocal of a number is $\dfrac{1}{\text{the number}}$.

Using the rules of fractions gives these results.

> The reciprocal of n is $\dfrac{1}{n}$.
>
> The reciprocal of $\dfrac{1}{n}$ is n.
>
> The reciprocal of $\dfrac{a}{b}$ is $\dfrac{b}{a}$.

To find reciprocals on a calculator, use the $\boxed{x^{-1}}$ button.

▍‖ EXAMPLE 1

Find the reciprocal of each of these.

a) $2\cdot5$ **b)** $\frac{1}{4}$ **c)** $\frac{2}{3}$

a) $\frac{1}{2\cdot5} = \frac{2}{5}$ or $0\cdot4$

b) $\frac{1}{4} = 4$

c) $\frac{2}{3} = 1\frac{1}{2}$ or $1\cdot5$

EXERCISE 15.1

 Do not use your calculator for questions **1** to **3**.

1 Write down the reciprocal of each of these numbers.

a) 5   **b)** 7

c) 20   **d)** 37

e) 250

2 Write down the number of which each of these is the reciprocal.

a) $\frac{1}{2}$ **b)** $\frac{1}{10}$

c) $\frac{1}{50}$ **d)** $\frac{1}{74}$

e) $\frac{1}{999}$

3 Calculate the reciprocal of each of these numbers, giving your answer as a fraction or a mixed number.

a) $\frac{3}{5}$ **b)** $\frac{7}{8}$

c) $1\frac{2}{3}$ **d)** $8\frac{1}{3}$

e) $\frac{4}{25}$

 You may use your calculator for question **4**.

4 Calculate the reciprocal of each of these numbers, giving your answer as a decimal.

a) 32   **b)** 1·6

c) 0·5   **d)** 1·25

e) 62·5

Prime factors

A prime number has as factors only 1 and itself.

The first prime numbers are 2, 3, 5, 7, 11, 13, 17, 19, …

Note that 1 is not a prime number.

To express a number in prime factor form, first divide by 2 until you get an odd number, then try to divide by 3, then by 5, and so on.

The divisors are always prime numbers.

EXAMPLE 2

Write 36 as a product of its prime factors.

```
2)36
2)18
3) 9
3) 3
   1
```

So, written as a product of its prime factors, 36 is $2 \times 2 \times 3 \times 3$, which can be written as $2^2 \times 3^2$.

ACTIVITY 1

Copy and complete this table up to $n = 36$, writing the prime factors in index form.

Number n	Prime factors in index form
2	2^1
3	3^1
4	2^2
5	5^1
6	$2^1 \times 3^1$
⋮	⋮
36	$2^2 \times 3^2$

The complete list of factors for 36 is
1, 2, 3, 4, 6, 9, 12, 18, 36.

We can write F(36) = 9, because 36 has nine factors.

But 36 is also equal to $2^2 \times 3^2$. Adding 1 to each of the indices, or powers, gives (2 + 1) and (2 + 1).

Multiplying these numbers gives
(2 + 1) × (2 + 1) = 3 × 3 = 9, which is the same value as F(36).

1 Investigate prime factors and the number of factors for numbers up to 36.
You might want to add a column to the table you have just completed.

Number n	Prime factors in index form	Number of factors
2	2^1	2
3	3^1	2
4	2^2	3
5	5^1	
6	$2^1 \times 3^1$	
⋮	⋮	⋮
36	$2^2 \times 3^2$	

Check to see if there is a link between the indices of the prime factors and the number of factors.

2 What do you notice about the numbers that have only two factors?

3 Which numbers have an odd number of factors?

STAGE

7

Factor tree method for finding prime factors

Rather than systematically dividing by prime numbers, you may prefer to use the factor tree method. In this method, you split the number into any two factors you spot, and then split those factors, continuing until all the factors are prime numbers.

For example, here is a factor tree for the number 126.

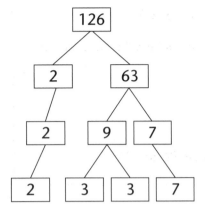

$126 = 2 \times 3 \times 3 \times 7 = 2 \times 3^2 \times 7$

A ACTIVITY 2

Use the factor tree method to find the prime factors of 64, 100, 144, 350, 540 and 72.

Highest common factor and lowest common multiple

When two or more numbers have been decomposed (split up) into their prime factors, these prime factors can be used to find the highest common factor and the lowest common multiple.

The highest common factor (HCF) of two numbers is the highest number that is a factor of both numbers.

The lowest common multiple (LCM) of two numbers is the lowest number that is a multiple of both numbers.

EXAMPLE 3

Find the highest common factor (HCF) of 96 and 180.

Finding the prime factors of each of the numbers, we obtain

$96 = 2^5 \times 3$ $96 = 2 \times 2 \times 2 \times 2 \times 2 \times 3$
$180 = 2^2 \times 3^2 \times 5$ $180 = 2 \times 2 \qquad\qquad \times 3 \times 3 \times 5$

To find the HCF, use the prime numbers that appear in *both* lists and use the *lower* power for each prime.

So the HCF is $2 \times 2 \times 3$.

The HCF of 96 and 180 is $2^2 \times 3 = 12$.

This means that 12 is the highest number that is a factor of both 96 and 180.

EXAMPLE 4

Find the lowest common multiple (LCM) of 96 and 180.

$96 = 2 \times 2 \times 2 \times 2 \times 2 \times 3$
$180 = 2 \times 2 \qquad\qquad \times 3 \times 3 \times 5$

To find the LCM, use *all* the prime numbers that appear in the lists and use the *higher* power for each prime.

So the LCM is $2 \times 2 \times 2 \times 2 \times 2 \times 3 \times 3 \times 5$.

The LCM of 96 and 180 is $2^5 \times 3^2 \times 5 = 1440$.

This means that 1440 is the lowest number that has both 96 and 180 as factors.
It is the lowest number that is a multiple of both 96 and 180.

EXERCISE 15.2

1 **a)** Express each of these numbers as a product of its prime factors.

    (i) 48   **(ii)** 72
    (iii) 210   **(iv)** 350
    (v) 75   **(vi)** 275
    (vii) 120   **(viii)** 198

  b) Use your results from part **a)** to find each of these.

    (i) the HCF of 48 and 72
    (ii) the LCM of 210 and 350
    (iii) the HCF of 75 and 275
    (iv) the LCM of 120 and 198

STAGE

7

EXERCISE 15.2 continued

2 a) Decompose each of these numbers into its prime factors.
  (i) 495   **(ii)** 260
  (iii) 2700   **(iv)** 1078
  (v) 420   **(vi)** 1125
  (vii) 112   **(viii)** 1960

b) Use your results from part **a)** to find each of these.
  (i) the HCF of 495 and 2700
  (ii) the LCM of 495 and 2700
  (iii) the HCF of 420 and 112
  (iv) the LCM of 420 and 1960

3 Find the prime factors of these numbers and use this to write down the HCF and LCM of each pair.
  a) 64 and 100
  b) 18 and 24
  c) 50 and 350
  d) 72 and 126

4 Find the HCF and the LCM of each pair of numbers.
  a) 27 and 63
  b) 20 and 50
  c) 48 and 84
  d) 50 and 64
  e) 42 and 49

5 Find the HCF and the LCM of each pair of numbers.
  a) 5544 and 2268
  b) 2016 and 10 584

C CHALLENGE 1

There are two lighthouses on a stretch of the coastline. The light in the first lighthouse flashes every 40 seconds. The light in the second lighthouse flashes every 15 seconds.

At 10 p.m. one evening, both lights are switched on.

What is the next time that the lights flash at the same time?

C CHALLENGE 2

Buses to Shenley leave the bus station every 40 minutes. Buses to Winley leave every 15 minutes.

At 8·15 a.m. buses to both Shenley and Winley leave the bus station.

When is the next time that buses to both places leave at the same time?

C CHALLENGE 3

Two numbers are **co-prime** if the only integer which 'goes into', or is a factor of, or is a divisor of, both of them is 1.

For example
- 3 and 7 are co-prime because the only factor they have in common is 1
- 4 and 6 are not co-prime because they share a common factor of 2
- 14 and 21 are not co-prime because they share a common factor of 7
- 5 and 23 are co-prime because they have no common factor except 1.

1 Try to find four pairs of numbers that are co-prime and four pairs of numbers that are not co-prime.

Look at all the positive integers less than 10.

1 2 3 4 5 6 7 8 9

Of these, 2, 4, 6 and 8 share a common factor of 2 with 10, and 5 divides into 10 and so is also a factor.

Therefore there are four numbers

1 3 7 9

that are less than 10 and are also co-prime with 10.

2 Copy this table and complete it for all the integers up to 24.

Integer n	Integers less than n and co-prime with it	Number of these integers
2	1	1
3	1, 2	2
4	1, 3	2
5	1, 2, 3, 4	4
6	1, 5	2
7	1, 2, 3, 4, 5, 6	6
$\vdots$	$\vdots$	$\vdots$
24	1, 5, 7, 11, 13, 17, 19, 23	8

What do you notice about the numbers in the right-hand column?

We can denote the number of integers which are less than n and co-prime with it by $C(n)$.
So $C(10) = 4$

3 a) Does $C(3) \times C(4) = C(12)$?
b) Does $C(2) \times C(6) = C(12)$?
c) Investigate whether $C(m) \times C(n) = C(mn)$.

STAGE
7

K KEY IDEAS

- The reciprocal of n is $\dfrac{1}{n}$.

- The reciprocal of $\dfrac{1}{n}$ is n.

- The reciprocal of $\dfrac{a}{b}$ is $\dfrac{b}{a}$.

- All positive integers can be decomposed into their prime factors.

- The highest common factor of two numbers is the highest number that is a factor of both numbers.

- The lowest common multiple of two numbers is the lowest number that is a multiple of both numbers.

Revision exercise C1

1 a) Copy and complete this table of values.

x	⁻1	0	1	2	3	4	5	6	7
x²									
− 6x									
+ 3									
y = x² − 6x + 3									

b) Draw the graph of $y = x^2 - 6x + 3$, for $x = {}^-1$ to 7.
Label the x-axis from ⁻1 to 7 and the y-axis from ⁻10 to 10.

c) Use the graph to find the values of x when y = 0.

2 The height, *h* metres, of a ball thrown upwards at 40 metres per second is given by the formula $h = 40t - 5t^2$, where *t* is the time in seconds.

a) Copy and complete this table of values.

t	0	1	2	3	4	5	6	7	8
t²									
40t									
− 5t²									
h = 40t − 5t²									

b) Draw the graph of $h = 40t - 5t^2$, for values of *t* from 0 to 8.

c) Find the times when the ball is 70 metres above the ground. Give your answers correct to 1 decimal place.

3 a) Draw the graph of $y = x^2 + 2x$, for values of x from ⁻4 to 2.

b) Use your graph to solve the equation $x^2 + 2x = 0$.

4 a) Draw the graph of $y = x^2 - 5x + 5$, for values of x from 0 to 5.

b) Use your graph to solve the equation $x^2 - 5x + 5 = 0$.

5 The table shows a summary of the marks gained by students in a test.

Marks (m)	Frequency
$0 \leqslant m < 10$	4
$10 \leqslant m < 20$	10
$20 \leqslant m < 30$	8
$30 \leqslant m < 40$	4

Calculate an estimate of the mean mark for the test.

6 Harry picked and measured some runner beans. These were their lengths.

Length (L cm)	Frequency
$10 < L \leqslant 15$	3
$15 < L \leqslant 20$	7
$20 < L \leqslant 25$	11
$25 < L \leqslant 30$	8
$30 < L \leqslant 35$	1

Calculate an estimate of the mean length of the runner beans.

7 Lisa timed her little brother when he was playing with his new toys over Christmas.

Time (t minutes)	Frequency
$0 \leqslant t < 10$	2
$10 \leqslant t < 20$	5
$20 \leqslant t < 30$	7
$30 \leqslant t < 40$	10
$40 \leqslant t < 50$	4

Calculate an estimate of the mean of these times.

STAGE 7

135

8 Kim and Petra asked their class, 'How much exercise have you had this week?' These were the results.

Time of exercise (h hours)	Number of people
$0 \leqslant h < 1$	3
$1 \leqslant h < 2$	8
$2 \leqslant h < 5$	12
$5 \leqslant h < 10$	5
$h \geqslant 10$	0

a) How many people were in the survey?
b) Calculate an estimate of the mean time of exercise.

9 Solve each of these inequalities and show the solution on a number line.
a) $2x > 5$
b) $x + 3 \leqslant 5$
c) $2x - 4 \geqslant x + 2$
d) $4x - 3 < 7 - x$
e) $4x - 9 \leqslant 2x + 7$

10 David has two brothers. One brother is two years younger than him and the other brother is five years older than him.
a) Let David be x years old. Write down an expression for the sum of their ages.
b) The sum of their ages is 39. Write down an equation and solve it to find x.
c) What are their ages?

11 Angela has £5 to spend. She spends £3·20 on her lunch and decides to buy as many 24p packets of crisps as possible with the rest of the money.
a) If the number of packets she buys is x, write down an inequality in x and solve it.
b) How many packets of crisps does she buy?

12 A quadrilateral has angles of $x°$, $3x°$, $90°$ and $(x + 20)°$.
a) Write down an equation in x and solve it.
b) What are the sizes of the angles?

13 A cyclist travels 5 km in 20 minutes. Calculate her speed in kilometres per hour.

14 A metal weight has a mass of 200 g and a density of 25 g/cm³. What is its volume?

15 Stephen runs a 100 m race in 13·58 seconds. Calculate his average speed. Give your answer to a sensible degree of accuracy.

16 Stanley has a population density of 5720 people/km². Its population is 47 500. What is the area of Stanley?

17 Find the reciprocal of each of these numbers.
a) 8
b) $\frac{1}{7}$
c) $\frac{2}{5}$
d) 0·8

18 **a)** Express each of these numbers as a product of its prime factors.
   (i) 84
   (ii) 540
b) Find the highest common factor of 84 and 540.

19 Find the lowest common multiple of 24 and 78.

Circles and tangents

You will learn about

- Finding the exact answer to a problem involving π
- The properties of tangents to circles
- Solving problems involving tangents to circles

You should already know

- The meaning of terms such as *chord, tangent* and *diameter*
- That the circumference of a circle is given by $2\pi r$ or πd
- That the area of a circle is given by πr^2
- Angle facts about triangles
- Symmetry facts about triangles
- The meaning of congruency

Using π without a calculator

When finding the area or the circumference of a circle, we need to use π.

Since $\pi = 3.141\,592\ldots$, we often don't substitute its value when working without a calculator.

An alternative is to give an exact answer by leaving π in the answer.

EXAMPLE 1

Find the circumference of a circle of radius $4\,\text{cm}$, leaving π in your answer.

$$\begin{aligned} \text{Circumference} &= 2\pi r \\ &= 2 \times \pi \times 4 \\ &= 8\pi \text{ cm} \end{aligned}$$

EXAMPLE 2

Find the area of a circle of radius 5 cm, leaving π in your answer.

Area = πr^2
   = $\pi \times 5^2$
   = $\pi \times 25$
   = $25\pi \, \text{cm}^2$

EXAMPLE 3

A circular pond of radius 3 m is surrounded by a path 2 m wide.

Find the area of the path. Give your answer as a multiple of π.

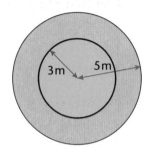

Area of path = area of large circle − area of small circle
   = $\pi \times 5^2 - \pi \times 3^2$
   = $25\pi - 9\pi$
   = $16\pi \, \text{m}^2$

EXERCISE 16.1

Give your answers to these questions as simply as possible.

Leave π in your answers where appropriate.

1   Simplify each of these.
   a) $2 \times 4 \times \pi$
   b) $\pi \times 8^2$
   c) $\pi \times 6^2$
   d) $2 \times 13 \times \pi$
   e) $\pi \times 9^2$

2   Simplify each of these.
   a) $4\pi + 10\pi$
   b) $\pi \times 8^2 + \pi \times 4^2$
   c) $\pi \times 6^2 - \pi \times 2^2$
   d) $2 \times 25\pi$
   e) $\dfrac{24\pi}{6\pi}$

3   The circumferences of two circles are in the ratio $10\pi : 4\pi$.
   Simplify this ratio.

4   Find the circumference of a circle of diameter 30 cm.

5   Find the area of a circle with radius 11 cm.

6   Find the circumference of a circle of radius 7 m.

7   Find the area of a circle with diameter 12 cm.

8   A circular flower bed of diameter 9 m has an edging strip put around its circumference.
   Find the length of edging strip needed.

EXERCISE 16.1 continued

9 A fish pond is a circle of radius 4 m. Work out the area of the surface of the fish pond.

10 A circular hole of radius 2 cm is drilled in a square of side length 8 cm. Find the area that is left.

C CHALLENGE 1

Find the area and perimeter of a semicircle of radius 5 cm.

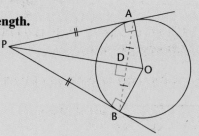

5 cm

Tangents to a circle

The diagram shows some important facts to remember about circles and tangents.

The angle between a tangent and the radius at the point of contact is 90°.

The two tangents from any point to a circle are equal in length.

The line OP bisects the chord AB at right angles.

Triangles APO and BPO are congruent.

Triangles AOD and BOD are congruent.

Triangles APD and BPD are congruent.

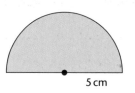

EXAMPLE 4

In the diagram above, angle APO = 35°. Calculate angle AOB.

Angle AOP = 180° − (35° + 90°) = 55°   (angle sum of triangle = 180°)
Angle BOP = 55°   (by symmetry)
So angle AOB = 110°.

EXAMPLE 5

Work out the size of angle OBA.

Give a reason for each step of your work.

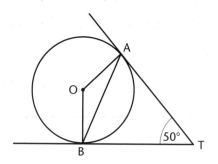

TA	= TB	(equal length tangents)
Angle TBA	= angle TAB	(base angles of an isosceles triangle)
Angle TBA	= $\frac{1}{2}(180° – 50°) = 65°$	(angle sum of a triangle = 180°)
Angle OBT	= 90°	(tangent perpendicular to radius)
Angle OBA	= 90° – 65° = 25°	

EXERCISE 16.2

Use this diagram for questions **1** to **10**.

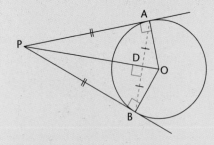

1 Find angle PAD when angle APO = 65°.

2 What shape is quadrilateral APBO?

3 Calculate angle AOB when angle APB = 46°.

4 Calculate angle OBD when angle BPO = 28°.

5 Explain how you can tell that angles DAO and APO are always equal.

6 Find angle AOP when angle APO = 65°.

7 Name three other angles in the diagram that are equal to angle PAD.

8 Calculate angle APB when angle AOB = 124°.

9 Calculate angle OBD when angle BPO = 28°.

10 Calculate angle ABP when angle APB = 108°.

CHALLENGE 2

A circle centre O has radius 5 cm. The length of a tangent from a point P to the circle is 12 cm.

a) Find the distance OP.

b) Find the shortest distance from P to the circle.

EXAM TIP
With right-angled triangles, you may need to use Pythagoras' theorem too.

 CHALLENGE 3

A chord in a circle of radius 7 cm is 3·5 cm from the centre of the circle.

Find the length of this chord, to the nearest millimetre.

 KEY IDEAS

- When using π you can give an exact answer by leaving π in the answer, simplifying the other numbers.

- The angle between a tangent and the radius at the point of contact is 90°.

- The two tangents from any point P to a circle centre O are equal in length.

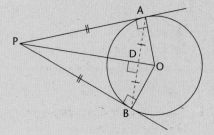

- When the tangents meet the circle at A and B, the line OP bisects the chord AB perpendicularly (at right angles).

- Triangles AOP and BOP are congruent.

STAGE

7

Changing the subject of a formula

You will learn about

- Rearranging a formula
- Solving a problem by rearranging a formula

You should already know

- How to simplify and solve linear equations

Rearranging formulae

Formulae can be treated in the same way as equations. This means they can be rearranged to change the subject.

EXAMPLE 1

Rearrange each of these formulae to make the letter in brackets the subject.

a) $a = b + c$ (b) **b)** $a = bx + c$ (b)

c) $n = m - 3s$ (s) **d)** $p = \dfrac{q + r}{s}$ (r)

a)
$$a = b + c$$
$$a - c = b \qquad \text{Subtract } c \text{ from both sides.}$$
$$b = a - c \qquad \text{Reverse to get } b \text{ on the left.}$$

b)
$$a = bx + c$$
$$a - c = bx \qquad \text{Subtract } c \text{ from both sides.}$$
$$\frac{a - c}{x} = b \qquad \text{Divide both sides by } x.$$
$$b = \frac{a - c}{x} \qquad \text{Reverse to get } b \text{ on the left.}$$

c)
$$n = m - 3s$$
$$n + 3s = m \qquad \text{Add } 3s \text{ to both sides.}$$
$$3s = m - n \qquad \text{Subtract } n \text{ from both sides.}$$
$$s = \frac{m - n}{3} \qquad \text{Divide both sides by } 3.$$

d)
$$p = \frac{q + r}{s}$$
$$sp = q + r \qquad \text{Multiply both sides by } s.$$
$$sp - q = r \qquad \text{Subtract } q \text{ from both sides.}$$
$$r = sp - q \qquad \text{Reverse to get } r \text{ on the left.}$$

EXAM TIP

If you have difficulty in rearranging a formula, practise by replacing some of the letters with numbers.

STAGE

7

EXAMPLE 2

The formula for the total cost, T, of entry to the cinema for three adults and three children is given by the formula $T = 3(a + c)$, where a is the price of an adult ticket and c is the price of a child ticket.

a) Make c the subject of the formula.

b) Find the cost for a child when the cost for an adult is £5 and the total cost is £24.

a) $T = 3(a + c)$

$T = 3a + 3c$ Multiply out the brackets.

$T - 3a = 3c$ Subtract $3a$ from both sides.

$\dfrac{T - 3a}{3} = c$ Divide both sides by 3.

$c = \dfrac{T - 3a}{3}$ Reverse to get c on the left.

b) $c = \dfrac{24 - 3 \times 5}{3} = \dfrac{24 - 15}{3} = \dfrac{9}{3} = 3$

The cost for a child is £3.

EXERCISE 17.1

1 Rearrange each formula to make the letter in the brackets the subject.

a) $a = b - c$ (b)

b) $3a = wx + y$ (x)

c) $v = u + at$ (t)

d) $A = \dfrac{T}{H}$ (T)

e) $C = P - 3T$ (T)

f) $P = \dfrac{u + v}{2}$ (u)

g) $C = 2\pi r$ (r)

h) $A = p(q + r)$ (q)

i) $p = q + 2r$ (q)

j) $B = s + 5r$ (r)

k) $s = 2u - t$ (t)

l) $m = \dfrac{pqr}{s}$ (q)

m) $L = 2G - 2F$ (G)

n) $F = \dfrac{m + 4n}{t}$ (n)

o) $T = \dfrac{S}{2a}$ (S)

p) $A = t(x - 2y)$ (y)

2 The formula for finding the perimeter P of a rectangle of length l and width w is $P = 2(l + w)$.

a) Rearrange the formula to make l the subject.

b) Find the length of a rectangle of width 8 metres and perimeter 44 metres.

3 The cost (£C) of catering for a wedding reception is given by the formula $C = A + 32n$, where A is the cost of the room and n is the number of guests.

a) Rearrange the formula to make n the subject.
b) Work out the number of guests when A is £120 and the total cost C is £1912.

4 The cooking time, T minutes, for w kg of meat is given by $T = 45w + 40$.
a) Make w the subject of this formula.
b) What is the value of w when the cooking time is 2 hours and 28 minutes?

5 The curved surface area (S cm^2) of a cylinder of radius r cm and height h cm is given by $S = 2\pi rh$.
a) Rearrange this formula to make r the subject.
b) Find the radius of a cylinder of height 4 cm, which has a curved surface area of 60·3 cm^2.

6 The formula for the volume V of a cone of height h and base radius r is $V = \frac{1}{3}\pi r^2 h$.

a) Rearrange the formula to make h the subject.
b) Find the height of a cone with base radius 9 cm and volume 2290 cm^3.

7 The cost (£C) of a minibus to the airport is given by the formula $C = 20 + \dfrac{d}{2}$, where d is the distance in miles.
a) Rearrange the formula to make d the subject.
b) Work out the distance when it costs £65 to go to the airport.

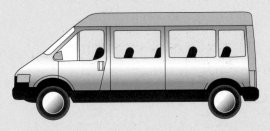

8 The cost (£C) of booking a coach for a party of n people is $C = 40 + 5n$.
a) Make n the subject of this formula.
b) Find the number of people when the cost is £235.

9 The total surface area (S cm^2) of a cylinder of radius r cm and height h cm is given by $S = 2\pi rh + 2\pi r^2$.
a) Rearrange this formula to make h the subject.
b) Find the height of a cylinder of radius 6 cm, which has a total surface area of 500 cm^2.

STAGE
7

17

C **CHALLENGE 1**

Rearrange each formula to make the letter in brackets the subject.

a) $A = 3r^2$ $\qquad$ (r)

b) $a^2 = b^2 + c^2$ $\qquad$ (c)

c) $T = 5\sqrt{g}$ $\qquad$ (g)

K **KEY IDEAS**

■ You can rearrange a formula using the same steps as you would if it were an equation with numbers instead of letters.

Equations and inequalities 2

You will learn about

- Solving equations and inequalities which contain brackets and the unknown on both sides of the equation
- Forming equations to solve problems

You should already know

- How to write a formula using letters
- How to collect together algebraic expressions
- How to expand brackets
- How to form and solve simple linear equations
- How to solve simple inequalities

Solving harder linear equations

Some linear equations you may be asked to solve may include decimals or have brackets.

EXAMPLE 1

Solve $2(5x - 4) = 3(x + 2)$.

$$2(5x - 4) = 3(x + 2)$$
$$10x - 8 = 3x + 6 \qquad \text{Multiply out the brackets.}$$
$$[10x - 8 + 8 = 3x + 6 + 8] \qquad \text{Add 8 to each side.}$$
$$10x = 3x + 14$$
$$[10x - 3x = 3x + 14 - 3x] \qquad \text{Subtract } 3x \text{ from each side.}$$
$$7x = 14$$
$$x = 14 \div 7 = 2 \qquad \text{Divide each side by 7.}$$

The lines in square brackets are often missed out.

18

EXAMPLE 2

Solve the equation $3{\cdot}6x = 8{\cdot}7$.

$3{\cdot}6x = 8{\cdot}7$
   $x = 8{\cdot}7 \div 3{\cdot}6$ Divide each side by $3{\cdot}6$.
   $x = 2{\cdot}416\ 666\ 6...$ Use a calculator and give the answer
                        to a suitable degree of accuracy.

   $x = 2{\cdot}42$ to 2 decimal places

> **EXAM TIP**
> The accuracy may be stated in the question.

EXERCISE 18.1

Solve these equations. Give your answers either exactly or correct to 2 decimal places.

1 $5(x - 2) = 4x$ **12** $5(x + 2) = 3(4 - x)$

2 $3(2x + 3) = 9$ **13** $5(x + 2) = 3(2x + 1)$

3 $4(2x - 3) = 3(x + 1)$ **14** $3{\cdot}5x = 9{\cdot}6$

4 $2(4x - 5) = 2x + 6$ **15** $5{\cdot}2x = 25$

5 $10(x + 2) = 3(x - 5)$ **16** $4{\cdot}6x = 7{\cdot}5$

6 $3(2x - 1) = 2(x + 4)$ **17** $2{\cdot}1(x - 3{\cdot}2) = 4{\cdot}4$

7 $2(3x - 5) = 14$ **18** $2{\cdot}2(2x + 5{\cdot}1) = 4{\cdot}9$

8 $4(3x - 1) = 10x$ **19** $2{\cdot}4x = 9{\cdot}7$

9 $3(2x + 1) = 7x + 1$ **20** $22x = 7{\cdot}55$

10 $5(2x - 2) = 2(x + 3)$ **21** $4{\cdot}2x = 9{\cdot}3$

11 $3(4x + 3) = 2(x + 6)$ **22** $2{\cdot}1(3x - 6{\cdot}4) = 9{\cdot}2$

STAGE
7

C CHALLENGE 1

Solve these equations.

a) $\dfrac{x}{2} = 3x - 10$ **b)** $\dfrac{3x}{2} = 7 - 2x$ **c)** $\dfrac{5x}{3} = x + 2$

d) $\dfrac{300}{x} = 15$ **e)** $\dfrac{75}{2x} = 3$

Solving inequalities

The inequalities in this chapter are more complicated than the ones you met in Chapter 13. For example, you may need to work with brackets.

EXAMPLE 3

Solve the inequality $x \geqslant 6x - 9$ and show the solution on a number line.

$$x \geqslant 6x - 9$$
$$x + 9 \geqslant 6x \qquad \text{Add 9 to each side.}$$
$$9 \geqslant 5x \qquad \text{Subtract } x \text{ from each side.}$$
$$1 \cdot 8 \geqslant x \qquad \text{Divide each side by 5.}$$
$$x \leqslant 1 \cdot 8 \qquad \text{Rewrite with } x \text{ as the subject.}$$

Notice that the inequality has changed direction too.
With inequalities you can't just swap sides.

EXAMPLE 4

Solve the inequality $2(3x - 1) > 4x + 7$.

$$2(3x - 1) > 4x + 7$$
$$6x - 2 > 4x + 7 \qquad \text{Multiply out the brackets.}$$
$$6x > 4x + 9 \qquad \text{Add 2 to each side.}$$
$$2x > 9 \qquad \text{Subtract } 4x \text{ from each side.}$$
$$x > 4\tfrac{1}{2} \qquad \text{Divide each side by 2.}$$

EXERCISE 18.2

Solve these inequalities.

1   $2x + 3 < 5$

2   $5x - 4 > 10 - 2x$

3   $3(2x - 1) > 15$

4   $4(x - 4) \geqslant x - 1$

5   $4n - 2 > 6$

6   $2n + 6 < n + 3$

7   $4n - 9 \geqslant 2n + 1$

8   $3(x - 1) \geqslant 6$

9   $2(3x - 1) > 4x + 6$

10   $2(x + 3) < 1 - 3x$

11   $3(2x - 1) \geqslant 11 - x$

12   $x + 4 > 2x$

STAGE

7

13 $2x - 5 < 4x + 1$

16 $2x - 1 > x - 4$

14 $3(x - 4) > 5(x + 1)$

17 $3(x + 3) \geqslant 2x - 1$

15 $x - 2 < 2x + 4$

18 $3(2x - 4) < 5(x - 6)$

Forming equations

Simple problems can be solved using equations.

||| **EXAMPLE 5**

The length of a rectangle is a cm, and the width is 15 cm shorter. The length is three times the width.

Write down an equation in a and solve it to find the length and width of the rectangle.

If the length = a, the width = $a - 15$ and the length = $3 \times$ width = $3(a - 15)$.
The equation is $a = 3(a - 15)$.

$$a = 3(a - 15)$$
$$a = 3a - 45 \qquad \text{Multiply out the brackets.}$$
$$[a + 45 = 3a - 45 + 45] \qquad \text{Add 45 to each side.}$$
$$a + 45 = 3a$$
$$[a + 45 - a = 3a - a] \qquad \text{Subtract } a \text{ from each side.}$$
$$45 = 2a$$
$$22 \cdot 5 = a \qquad \text{Divide each side by 2.}$$
$$a = 22 \cdot 5 \qquad \text{Rewrite with the subject on the left-hand side.}$$

So the length = $22 \cdot 5$ cm and the width = $7 \cdot 5$ cm.

EXAM TIP

When you are asked to set up an equation and solve it, you will not get any marks if you just give the answer without the equation.

STAGE

7

EXERCISE 18.3

1 Two angles in a triangle are x and $2x - 30°$. The first angle is twice the size of the second.
Set up an equation and solve it to find the size of the two angles.

2 The width of a rectangle is 3 cm and the length is $x + 4$ cm. The area is $27\,\text{cm}^2$.
Set up an equation and solve it to find x.

3 In a class of 32 students, x are girls. There are three times as many girls as boys.
Set up an equation and solve it to find how many boys and how many girls there are.

4 Stephen thinks of a number. If he doubles the number and then subtracts 5, he gets the same answer as if he subtracts 2 from the number and then multiplies by 3.
Let the number be n. Set up an equation and solve it to find n.

5 On a bus trip, each child pays £p and each adult pays £12 more than this. There are 28 children and four adults on the bus. The same amount of money is collected from all the children as from all the adults.
Set up an equation and solve it to find how much each child and each adult pays.

6 At Joe's Diner, one-course meals cost £x. Two-course meals cost £2 more. A group of eight people bought three one-course meals and five two-course meals. They paid £38 altogether.
Set up an equation and solve it to find the cost of a one-course meal.

7 Two angles of a pentagon are $x°$ and the other three are each $(2x - 20)°$. The total of all the angles is 540°.
Write down an equation and solve it to find the size of each angle.

8 The cost per person of a flight from Sheffield Airport is the charge made by the airline plus £40 tax. Four people flew from Sheffield to Cairo and the total they had to pay was £1640.
Let the charge made by the airline be £x. Write down an equation in x and solve it to find the charge made by the airline.

9 A 32-year-old man has three children who are x, $2x$ and $(2x + 4)$ years old. The man is four times as old as his eldest child.
Set up an equation and solve it to find the ages of the children.

10 At Deno's Pizza Place, a basic pizza costs £x and extra toppings are 50p each. Bernard and four of his friends each have pizzas with two extra toppings. They pay £25·50.
Set up an equation and find the cost of a basic pizza.

STAGE

7

151

C CHALLENGE 2

Bev is x years old.

Mike is ten years older than Bev.

The sum of their ages is less than 83.

What is the oldest Bev can be?

K KEY IDEAS

■ To solve an equation or inequality, you must do the same to both sides.

■ To solve harder equations and inequalities, do one step at a time.

■ Some problems can be solved by setting up and solving an equation.

Loci 19

You will learn about

- What a locus is
- Constructing the locus of points that are a fixed distance from a given point or line, or equidistant from two fixed points or two intersecting lines, or the shortest distance from a line
- Solving problems that involve one or more loci

You should already know

- How to use a protractor and compasses
- How to construct a triangle, given three sides
- How to construct a triangle, given two sides and an angle
- How to construct a triangle, given two angles and a side
- How to make scale drawings

Constructing loci

ACTIVITY 1

A farmer wants to plant crops but he must keep at least 1 m from the borders of his field.

Trace this diagram.

Sketch the region where he can plant crops.

The local walkers' group have agreed to get a footpath constructed starting at gate G_1 which is equidistant from the two hedges h_1 and h_2.

Construct this path.

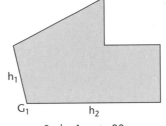

Scale: 1 cm to 20 m

STAGE
7

> The *locus* of a point is the path or the region that the point covers as it moves according to a particular rule. The plural of locus is *loci*.

Simple loci

> The locus of points that are a fixed distance from a given point is a circle, centred at the given point.

This means that the locus of a point 3 cm from A is a circle, centre A and radius 3 cm.

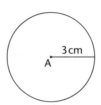

The locus of a point less than (<) 3 cm from A is the region inside a circle, centre A and radius 3 cm.

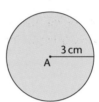

The locus of a point greater than (>) 3 cm from A is the region outside a circle, centre A and radius 3 cm.

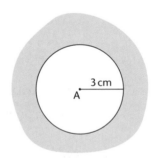

> The locus of points that are a fixed distance from a given line is a pair of parallel lines.

For example, the locus of a point 2 cm from a straight line is a pair of lines parallel to that line, 2 cm away from it on either side.

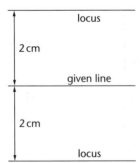

EXAMPLE 1

A line is 6 cm long.
Construct the locus
of all the points that
are 2 cm from the line.

The locus is two
parallel lines with a
semicircle joining
them at each end.

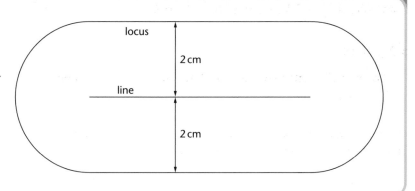

The perpendicular bisector of a line

**The locus of a point that stays an equal distance from two points
is the perpendicular bisector of the line joining the two points.**

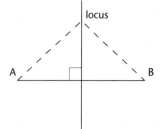

Construction

Draw the line AB.

Open the compasses to a radius that is more than half the length of AB.

Put your compass point at A and draw two arcs, above and
below the line.

Keep the compasses set to the same radius.

Put the compass point at B and draw two arcs, above and
below the line.

Join the two points where the pairs of arcs cross.

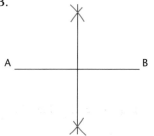

EXAMPLE 2

Two towns P and Q are 5 kilometres apart.
Draw a diagram and shade the region that is
nearer to P than Q.
Use a scale of 1 cm to 1 km.

Mark P and Q 5 cm apart. Draw the
perpendicular bisector of the line PQ and
shade the region on P's side of the line.
The shading could go beyond P and further
up or down the page.

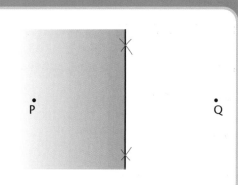

A ACTIVITY 2

a) (i) Draw a triangle. Make it big enough to fill about half of your page.

(ii) Construct the perpendicular bisector of each of the three sides.

(iii) If you have drawn them accurately, the three bisectors should all meet at one point.
Put your compass point on this point, and the pencil on one of the corners of the triangle. Draw a circle.

b) You have drawn the **circumcircle** of the triangle.
What do you notice about this circle?

The bisector of an angle

> **The locus of a point that stays an equal distance from two intersecting lines is the pair of lines that bisect the angles between the lines.**

Can you see why this is so?

Drawing the perpendiculars to the lines from a point on the locus creates two congruent triangles.

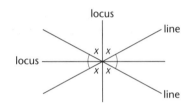

Construction

Draw an angle and mark the vertex A.

Put your compass point at A and draw an arc to cut the lines forming the angle at B and C.

Put the point at B and draw an arc in the angle.

Keep the compasses set to the same radius.

Put the point at C and draw an arc in the angle to cut the arc just drawn.

Draw a straight line through A and the point where the arcs cross.

The bisector could be continued to the left of A. If the lines are extended, another bisector could be drawn, perpendicular to the first one.

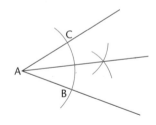

EXAM TIP

The locus of the points equidistant from two intersecting lines is a pair of lines, but usually you only require one.

EXAMPLE 3

Draw a triangle ABC with sides AB = 5 cm and AC = 4 cm, and angle A = 50°.

Use compasses to bisect angle A. Shade in the locus of the points inside the triangle that are nearer to AB than AC.

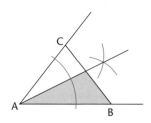

The perpendicular from a point to a line

Construction

Use the following method to construct the perpendicular from point P to the given line.

1 Open your compasses to any radius. Put your compass point on P. Draw two arcs, cutting the line at Q and R.

2 Keep the compasses set to the same radius. Put the compass point on Q. Draw an arc below the line. Now put the compass point on R and draw another arc, cutting the first arc at X.

3 Line up your ruler with points P and X. Draw the line PM. This line is at right angles to the original line.

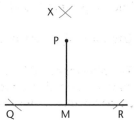

A ACTIVITY 3

a) (i) Draw a line across your page. Put a cross on one side of the line and label it P.

(ii) Construct the perpendicular from P to the line. Make sure you keep your compasses set to the same radius all the time.
This time, join P to X: don't stop at the original line.

b) (i) Measure PM and XM. What do you notice?

(ii) What can you say about P and X?

EXERCISE 19.1

1 Draw a circle, centre A and radius 5 cm. Shade the locus of the points that are less than 5 cm from A.

2 Draw a rectangle 4 cm by 5 cm. Sketch the locus of the points outside the rectangle that are 1 cm from the perimeter of the rectangle.

3 Draw a rectangle ABCD with AB = 6 cm and BC = 4 cm. Sketch the locus of the points inside the rectangle that are nearer to A than B.

4 Draw two parallel lines across the page, 4 cm apart. Draw the locus of the points that are 1 cm from the top line and 3 cm from the bottom line.

5 A fox never travels more than 5 miles from its den. Draw a sketch to show the region where it travels.

6 Draw a line 7 cm long. Construct the perpendicular bisector of the line.

7 Draw an angle of 70°. Construct the bisector of the angle.

8 Show, by shading, the locus of the points that are more than 4 cm from a fixed point A.

9 Draw a line 6 cm long. Show, by shading in a sketch, the locus of the points that are less than 2 cm from the line.

10 Draw an angle of 80°. Construct the bisector of the angle.

11 Draw a line AB 6 cm long. Construct the perpendicular bisector of AB.

12 Draw a line 10 cm long. Put a point anywhere above the line. Construct the perpendicular from your point to the line.

13 Construct a triangle ABC with AB = 8 cm, AC = 7 cm and BC = 5 cm. Use compasses and a ruler to bisect angle A. Shade the locus of the points inside the triangle that are nearer to AB than AC.

EXERCISE 19.1 continued

14 Draw a square ABCD with sides of 6 cm.
Construct the locus of the points that are equidistant from A and C.
What do you notice about the locus?

15 Draw a triangle ABC with AB = 8 cm, angle A = 90° and angle B = 40°.
Do a construction to find the locus of the points inside the triangle that are nearer to AC than BC.

16 Draw a square with sides of 4 cm.
Label one corner A.
Show the locus of the points inside the square that are less than 3 cm from A.

17 Draw a rectangle ABCD with sides AB = 7 cm and BC = 5 cm.
Use compasses to construct the line equidistant from AB and AC.

18 Construct the triangle ABC with angle A = 30°, angle B = 50° and AB = 10 cm.
Construct the locus of the points equidistant from A and B.

19 Two towns Bimouth and Tritown are 10 miles apart. Phoebe wants to live nearer to Bimouth than Tritown.
Using a scale of 1 cm : 2 miles, make a scale drawing and show, by shading, the region where she can live.

20 Draw a triangle ABC with AB = 7 cm, angle A = 50° and angle B = 40°.
Show, by shading, the locus of the points within the triangle that are nearer to AC than BC.

21 Sonia has a 20 metre cable on her lawnmower and the socket is in the middle of the back wall of her house.
The back of the house is 12 m wide and her garden is a rectangle the same width as the house, stretching 24 m from the house.
Using a scale of 1 cm : 4 m, make a drawing of her garden and show, by shading, the region she can reach with the mower.

EXAM TIP

In most cases you will be asked to construct a locus either to size or to scale. Draw it as accurately as you can. Do not stop the line of a construction at the intersection of the arcs: draw it through the intersection. When you do a construction, leave in your construction lines.

CHALLENGE 1

Draw a circle of radius 5 cm. Draw a chord of the circle which is 6 cm long.

Construct the perpendicular from the centre of the circle on to the chord.

Measure the length of each of the two parts of the chord. What do you notice?

STAGE
7

Problems involving intersection of loci

Combining all you know about loci, you can answer more complicated questions involving more than one locus.

EXAMPLE 4

Construct triangle ABC with AB = 7 cm, AC = 6 cm and BC = 4 cm.

By using constructions, find the point that is equidistant from all three vertices. Label this point D.

First you need the line equidistant from two vertices. If you choose vertices A and B, you need to construct the perpendicular bisector of AB.

Then you need to construct the perpendicular bisector of another side. Where they cross is the required point.

This diagram is half-size.

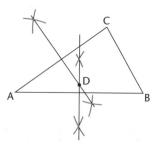

You could also bisect the third side, and that line would also pass through the same point.

EXAMPLE 5

Two points A and B are 4 cm apart.

Show, by shading, the locus of the points that are less than 2·5 cm from A, and nearer to B than A.

You need to draw a circle, radius 2·5 cm and centre A. You also need to draw the bisector of the line AB. The region you require is inside the circle and on the B side of the bisector.

The required region is shaded on the diagram.

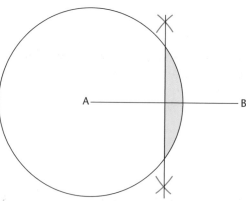

EXAMPLE 6

Erica wants to put a rocking chair in her room. She wants the chair more than 0·5 m from a wall and less than 2 m from corner A. This is a sketch of her room.

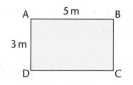

Using a scale of 1 cm : 1 m, make a scale drawing of the room and show, by shading, the region where the chair can be placed.

Draw the rectangle and then add lines 0·5 cm from each side. Draw a circle, centre A and radius 2 cm.

In this diagram the regions not required are shaded, leaving the white region where the chair can be placed.

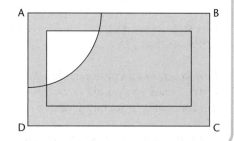

EXAMPLE 7

Find the centre of the rotation that maps triangle ABC on to triangle A'B'C'.

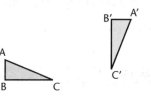

The centre of rotation must be equidistant from A and A'. It will be on the perpendicular bisector of AA'. Arcs have been omitted to make the diagram clearer.

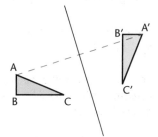

The centre must also be equidistant from C and C'. The centre of rotation will be the point where the two perpendicular bisectors cross.

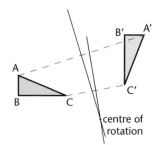

The centre must also be equidistant from B and B'. Construct the perpendicular bisector of BB' to check.

STAGE

7

Draw all of these accurately.

1 Two points A and B are 5 cm apart. Show, by shading, the region that is less than 3 cm from A, and more than 4 cm from B.

2 A rectangle ABCD has sides AB = 5 cm and BC = 4 cm. Draw the rectangle and show, by shading, the region inside the rectangle that is nearer to AB and CD, and less than 3·5 cm from B.

3 Draw a triangle ABC with AB = 6 cm, angle A = 60° and angle B = 55°. Use constructions to find the point D that is equidistant from all three sides.

4 Draw a rectangle ABCD with sides AB = 4 cm and BC = 3 cm. Show the points that are equidistant from AB and BC, and 3·5 cm from A.

5 Draw a triangle ABC with sides AB = 9 cm, BC = 6 cm and AC = 5 cm. Show, by shading, the region inside the triangle that is nearer to AB than BC, and more than 3 cm from C.

6 Show, by shading, the locus of the points that are more than 2 cm from a point A and less than 3 cm from point A.

7 Two points A and B are 4 cm apart. Show, by shading, the locus of all the points that are less than 2·5 cm from A, and more than 3 cm from B.

8 Draw a triangle ABC with AB = 6 cm, angle A = 40° and angle B = 35°. Use constructions to find the point D that is equidistant from A and B, and 4 cm from C.

9 Draw a square with sides of 4 cm. Show, by shading, the region within the square that is more than 2 cm from every vertex.

10 Draw a triangle ABC with AB = 6 cm, AC = 5 cm and angle A = 55°. Bisect angle A. Draw the perpendicular bisector of AB. Show, by shading, the region that is inside the triangle, nearer to AB than AC, and nearer to B than A.

11 Two towns, Hilldon and Baton are 20 miles apart. It is proposed to build a new shopping centre within 15 miles of Hilldon but nearer to Baton than Hilldon. Using a scale of 1 cm : 5 miles, make a drawing and show the region where the shopping centre can be built.

12 Richard's bedroom is rectangular with sides of 4 m and 6·5 m. He wants to put a desk within 1 metre of a longer wall and within 2.5 m of the centre of the window in the middle of one of the shorter walls. Using a scale of 1 cm : 1 m, make a scale drawing and show, by shading, the region where the desk can be placed.

13 Kirsty has a triangular patio with sides of 6 m, 4 m and 5 m. She wants to put a plant pot on the patio more than 2 m from any corner. Using a scale of 1 cm : 1 m, make a drawing and show, by shading, where she can put the plant pot.

EXAM TIP

You can either shade the required region or shade the regions that are *not* required. It is often easier to do the latter if the regions are at all complicated. Give a key or label the diagram to make it clear which you have done.

14 This is a sketch of a plot of land that Arun wants to use for camping.

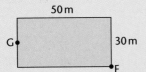

He wants to put a tap in the field within 35 m of the gate, which is at the middle of one of the shorter sides. He also wants the tap to be within 25 m of his farm, which is at corner F.
Using a scale of 1 cm : 10 m, make a scale drawing of the land. Show, by shading, the position where the tap can be placed.

15 A field is a quadrilateral ABCD with AB = 25 m, BC = 30 m, angle A = 90°, angle B = 106° and angle C = 65°.
The farmer wants to put a scarecrow within 15 m of corner A and nearer to CD than CB.
Using a scale of 1 cm to 5 m, draw the field and show, by shading, the region where the scarecrow can be placed.

16 Dave and Clare live 7 miles apart. They set out on bikes to meet. They ride directly towards each other. When they meet, Dave has ridden less than 5 miles and Clare has ridden less than 4 miles.
Using a scale of 1 cm : 1 mile, make a scale drawing to show where they could have met.

17 Tariq's garden is a rectangle ABCD with AB = 10 m and BC = 4 m. He wants to put a rotary washing line in the garden. It must be more than 4 m from corner C and more than 1 m from side AB.
Using a scale of 1 cm : 1 m, make a scale drawing of the garden and show where he can put the rotary washing line.

18 The distances between three towns Arbridge, Beaton and Ceborough are AB = 25 miles, AC = 40 miles and BC = 30 miles. A new petrol station is to be built as near as possible to all three towns.
Using a scale of 1 cm : 5 miles, make constructions to find the point D where the petrol station should be placed.

19 Sasha has a rectangular garage measuring 2 m by 5 m. It has a door at one end. She wants to put a hook in the ceiling. It must be midway between the two longer sides, less than 3·5 m from the door end and less than 2·5 m from the other end.
Make a scale drawing of the ceiling using a scale of 1 cm : 1 m. Show, by shading, the region where the hook can be fixed.

20 This is a sketch of the playing field in Towbridge.

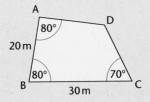

A new swing is to be placed in the field. It must be within 15 m of A and nearer to AB than AD.
Use a scale of 1 cm : 5 m to make a scale drawing and show the region where the swing can be placed.

21 A sailor is shipwrecked at night. She is 140 m from the straight coastline. She swims straight for the shore.
a) Make a scale drawing of the path she swims.
The coastguard is standing on the beach exactly where the sailor will come ashore. He has a searchlight that can illuminate up to a distance of 50 m.
b) Mark on your diagram the part of the sailor's swim that will be lit up.

STAGE

7

K KEY IDEAS

- The locus of a point is the path or the region that the point covers as it moves according to a particular rule.

- The locus of a point x cm from point A is a circle with centre A and radius x cm.

- The locus of a point x cm from a line is a pair of lines parallel to the given line, x cm on either side of it.

- The locus of a point equidistant from two points A and B is the perpendicular bisector of the line AB.

- The locus of a point equidistant from two non-parallel lines is the bisector(s) of the angle(s) between the lines.

- The shortest distance from a point to a line is the perpendicular distance.

Decimals 20

You should already know

- How to turn fractions into decimal equivalents
- The decimal equivalents of simple fractions, for example $\frac{1}{2}$, $\frac{1}{4}$ and $\frac{3}{4}$
- How to multiply simple decimals and whole numbers

Multiplying and dividing decimals

 ACTIVITY 1

a) $39 \times 8 = 312$

Without using your calculator, write down the answers to these multiplications.

(i) 3.9×8
(ii) 39×0.8
(iii) 0.39×8
(iv) 0.39×0.8

b) $37 \times 56 = 2072$

Without using your calculator, write down the answers to these multiplications.

(i) 3.7×56 (ii) 37×5.6 (iii) 3.7×5.6
(iv) 0.37×56 (v) 0.37×5.6 (vi) 0.37×0.56

Now check your answers with your calculator.

STAGE
7

165

Decimals

Look again at your answers to Activity 1.

These are the steps you take to multiply decimals.

> 1 **Carry out the multiplication, ignoring the decimal points. The digits in this answer will be the same as the digits in the final answer.**
>
> 2 **Count the total number of decimal places in the two numbers to be multiplied.**
>
> 3 **Place the decimal point into your answer from step 1 so that the final answer has the same number of decimal places as you found in step 2.**

EXAMPLE 1

Work out 8×0.7.

1 First do $8 \times 7 = 56$.

2 The total number of decimal places in 8 and 0·7 is $0 + 1 = 1$.

3 The answer is 5·6.

> **EXAM TIP**
>
> Notice that when you multiply by a number between 0 and 1, such as 0·7, the answer is smaller than the original number (5·6 is smaller than 8).

EXAMPLE 2

Work out 8.3×3.4.

1 First do 83×34.

$$\begin{array}{r} 83 \\ \times 34 \\ \hline 2490 \\ 332 \\ \hline 2822 \end{array}$$

The method used here is the traditional 'long multiplication'. You may prefer another method.

2 The total number of decimal places in 8·3 and 3·4 is $1 + 1 = 2$.

3 The answer is 28·22.

EXAMPLE 3

Work out 8.32×2.6.

1 First do 832×26.

$$
\begin{array}{r}
832 \\
\times \quad 26 \\
\hline
16\,640 \\
4\,992 \\
\hline
21\,632
\end{array}
$$

2 The total number of decimal places in 8.32 and 2.6 is $2 + 1 = 3$.

3 The answer is 21.632.

ACTIVITY 2

a) Do these calculations on your calculator.

    (i) $26 \div 1.3$ **(ii)** $260 \div 13$

b) What do you notice?

c) Now do these calculations on your calculator.

    (i) $5.92 \div 3.7$ **(ii)** $59.2 \div 37$
    (iii) $3.995 \div 2.35$ **(iv)** $399.5 \div 235$

d) Can you explain your results?

The result of a division is unchanged when you multiply both numbers by 10 (i.e. move the decimal point one place in both numbers).

The result is also unchanged when you multiply both numbers by 100 (i.e. move the decimal point two places in both numbers).

This rule is exactly the same as when you are writing equivalent fractions.

For example, $\frac{3}{5} = \frac{30}{50} = \frac{300}{500}$.

You use this rule when you are dividing decimals.

EXAMPLE 4

Work out $6 \div 0.3$.

First multiply both numbers by 10, so that the number you are dividing by is a whole number.

The calculation becomes $60 \div 3$.

$60 \div 3 = 20$
$6 \div 0.3$ is also 20.

> **EXAM TIP**
> Notice that when you divide by a number between 0 and 1, such as 0.3, the answer is larger than the original number (20 is larger than 6).

EXAMPLE 5

Work out $4.68 \div 0.4$.

First multiply both numbers by 10 (move the decimal point one place).
The calculation becomes $46.8 \div 4$.

$$4 \overline{)46.^28} \quad \begin{array}{c} 11.7 \end{array}$$

The decimal point in the answer goes above the decimal point in 46.8.

$4.68 \div 0.4$ is also 11.7.

EXAMPLE 6

Work out $3.64 \div 1.3$.

First multiply both numbers by 10 (move the decimal point one place).

The calculation becomes $36.4 \div 13$.

$$13 \overline{)36.^{10}4} \quad \begin{array}{c} 2.8 \end{array}$$

You may have been taught to do this by long division rather than by short division.

$3.64 \div 1.3$ is also 2.8.

EXERCISE 20.1

1 Work out these multiplications.
 a) 0.47×6
 b) 4.8×4
 c) 7×1.04
 d) 1.32×0.5
 e) 2.1×1.8
 f) 9.3×1.5
 g) 8.2×1.6
 h) 3.2×0.14
 i) 9.6×0.09
 j) 4.8×0.25
 k) 11.3×3.12
 l) 21×1.45
 m) 9.85×1.67
 n) 0.57×0.342
 o) 0.23×7.85

2 Work out these divisions.
 a) $13.6 \div 4$
 b) $11.4 \div 3$
 c) $27.2 \div 0.8$
 d) $40.5 \div 0.9$
 e) $5.28 \div 0.03$
 f) $7.25 \div 0.5$
 g) $8.54 \div 0.7$
 h) $6.36 \div 0.06$
 i) $0.85 \div 0.05$
 j) $2.52 \div 0.09$
 k) $19.2 \div 1.2$
 l) $71.4 \div 0.21$
 m) $1.95 \div 0.15$
 n) $3.6 \div 2.4$
 o) $2.88 \div 0.018$

CHALLENGE 1

In a 4 by 400 m relay race, the four members of a team ran these times.

44·5 seconds, 45·6 seconds, 45·8 seconds, 43·9 seconds

What was their average time?

CHALLENGE 2

a) Calculate the area of this rectangle.

6·3 cm

2·6 cm

b) This rectangle has the same area as the one in part **a)**.

Calculate the length of this rectangle.

3·9 cm

STAGE

7

A **ACTIVITY 3**

Write each of these fractions as a decimal.

$\frac{2}{3}$, $\frac{1}{5}$, $\frac{2}{11}$, $\frac{3}{4}$, $\frac{3}{7}$, $\frac{5}{6}$, $\frac{1}{18}$, $\frac{1}{20}$, $\frac{5}{8}$

What do you notice about the decimal values?

EXAMPLE 7

Convert $\frac{5}{8}$ to a decimal.

$\frac{5}{8} = 5 \div 8 = 0{\cdot}625$

EXAMPLE 8

Convert $\frac{1}{6}$ to a decimal.

$\frac{1}{6} = 1 \div 6 = 0{\cdot}16666...$

Look again at Examples 7 and 8.

In Example 7, the decimal equivalent of $\frac{5}{8}$ is exactly $0{\cdot}625$. This is an example of a **terminating decimal**. It is called terminating because it finishes at the digit 5.

In Example 8, the decimal equivalent of $\frac{1}{6}$ goes on forever with the digit 6 repeating itself over and over again. This is an example of a **recurring decimal**.

The dot notation for recurring decimals

To save a lot of writing, there is a special notation for recurring decimals. You put a dot over the figure that recurs.

So, for example, $\frac{1}{3} = 0{\cdot}333\,333...$ is written as $0{\cdot}\dot{3}$.

Similarly, $\frac{1}{6} = 0{\cdot}166\,666...$ is written as $0{\cdot}1\dot{6}$.

EXAMPLE 9

Write $\frac{7}{11}$ as a recurring decimal.

$7 \div 11 = 0{\cdot}636\,363...$

This time both the 6 and 3 recur. To show this you put a dot over both the 6 and the 3. That is, you write $0{\cdot}\dot{6}\dot{3}$.

EXAMPLE 10

Write $\frac{171}{333}$ as a recurring decimal.

$171 \div 333 = 0 \cdot 513\,513\,513...$

This time there are three figures that recur. You write this as $0 \cdot \dot{5}1\dot{3}$. Put a dot over the first and last figures that recur.

This means that $0 \cdot 432\,513\,251\,325\,1$, for example, is written as $0 \cdot 43\dot{2}5\dot{1}$.

Sometimes, because so many figures recur, it is difficult to see the recurring figures on a calculator. For example, $\frac{3}{7}$ will be shown as $0 \cdot 428\,571\,428$ on many calculators. It is only just noticeable that this means all six digits will recur.

That is, $\frac{3}{7} = 0 \cdot 428\,571\,428\,571\,428\,57... = 0 \cdot \dot{4}28\,57\dot{1}$.

On calculators which show fewer digits, it may be even less obvious.

ACTIVITY 4

Use your calculator to work out $\frac{1}{7}, \frac{2}{7}, \frac{3}{7}, ... \frac{6}{7}$.

What do you notice about the digits in your answer?

Check the patterns for other fractions which are recurring decimals.

CHALLENGE 3

What can you say about the numbers in the denominators of the fractions that give terminating decimals?

STAGE

7

EXERCISE 20.2

Convert each of the fractions in questions **1** to **32** to a decimal. When the answer is a recurring decimal, use the dot notation.

1 $\frac{3}{8}$

2 $\frac{5}{6}$

3 $\frac{5}{16}$

4 $\frac{11}{40}$

5 $\frac{5}{9}$

6 $\frac{17}{25}$

7 $\frac{5}{27}$

8 $\frac{16}{33}$

9 $\frac{7}{110}$

10 $\frac{7}{111}$

11 $\frac{79}{250}$

12 $\frac{79}{2500}$

13 $\frac{5}{7}$

14 $\frac{79}{222}$

15 $\frac{19}{11}$

16 $\frac{73}{64}$

17 $\frac{7}{8}$

18 $\frac{7}{9}$

19 $\frac{9}{11}$

20 $\frac{7}{32}$

21 $\frac{3}{80}$

22 $\frac{17}{36}$

23 $\frac{29}{125}$

24 $\frac{23}{60}$

25 $\frac{37}{64}$

26 $\frac{57}{132}$

27 $\frac{7}{54}$

28 $\frac{576}{625}$

29 $\frac{457}{1111}$

30 $\frac{457}{1110}$

31 $\frac{1}{303}$

32 $\frac{813}{11\,111}$

33 Given that $\frac{1}{27} = 0\cdot0\dot{3}\dot{7}$, $\frac{1}{3} = 0\cdot\dot{3}$ and $\frac{1}{11} = 0\cdot\dot{0}\dot{9}$, find the decimal equivalent of each of these without using a calculator.

a) $\frac{2}{27}$ **b)** $\frac{5}{27}$

c) $\frac{2}{3}$ **d)** $\frac{2}{11}$

e) $\frac{5}{11}$ **f)** $\frac{6}{11}$

34 Put each set of fractions into ascending order (smallest first).

a) $\frac{1}{3}, \frac{3}{10}, \frac{5}{18}, \frac{4}{11}, \frac{2}{7}, \frac{7}{19}, \frac{2}{5}, \frac{9}{24}$

b) $\frac{3}{5}, \frac{3}{4}, \frac{1}{2}, \frac{5}{9}, \frac{4}{7}, \frac{11}{18}, \frac{8}{15}$

Decimals to fractions

All terminating and recurring decimals have fraction equivalents.

Example 11 illustrates the method of changing a terminating decimal to a fraction.

EXAMPLE 11

Find the equivalent fraction to 0·624.

From the definitions of the columns in decimals,

$$0 \cdot 624 = \frac{6}{10} + \frac{2}{100} + \frac{4}{1000}$$

$$= \frac{600}{1000} + \frac{20}{1000} + \frac{4}{1000}$$

$$= \frac{624}{1000}$$

$$= \frac{78}{125} \qquad \text{(dividing top and bottom by 8).}$$

The quick method is simply to write 624 over 1000 straight away, since the 4 represents 'four thousandths'.

EXAMPLE 12

Convert each of these to a fraction.

a) 0·48 **b)** 0·035

a) $0 \cdot 48 = \frac{48}{100} = \frac{12}{25}$

b) $0 \cdot 035 = \frac{35}{1000} = \frac{7}{200}$

Converting recurring decimals to fractions is more difficult and the general method will be dealt with later in the course. Only simple cases are dealt with here.

These ones are worth remembering.

$$0 \cdot \dot{3} = \frac{1}{3} \qquad \text{and} \qquad 0 \cdot \dot{6} = \frac{2}{3}$$

so $0 \cdot 0\dot{3} = \frac{1}{30}$ and $0 \cdot 0\dot{6} = \frac{2}{30} = \frac{1}{15}.$

$$0 \cdot \dot{1} = \frac{1}{9}, \qquad 0 \cdot \dot{2} = \frac{2}{9}, \qquad 0 \cdot \dot{4} = \frac{4}{9}, \qquad \text{and so on}$$

so $0 \cdot 0\dot{1} = \frac{1}{90}, \qquad 0 \cdot 0\dot{2} = \frac{2}{90}, \qquad 0 \cdot 0\dot{4} = \frac{4}{90}, \qquad \text{and so on.}$

STAGE

7

EXERCISE 20.3

Convert each of the decimals in questions **1** to **20** to a fraction in its lowest terms.

1 0·7

2 0·29

3 0·85

4 0·07

5 0·312

6 0·255

7 0·056

8 0·008

9 0·8

10 0·37

11 0·68

12 0·02

13 0·545

14 0·892

15 0·018

16 0·1345

17 0·$\dot{7}$

18 0·0$\dot{7}$

19 0·$\dot{8}$

20 0·00$\dot{8}$

21 Given that $0\cdot\dot{1} = \frac{1}{9}$, write each of these as a fraction.
   a) 0·$\dot{2}$
   b) 0·$\dot{3}$
   c) 0·$\dot{5}$

22 Given that $0\cdot\dot{0}1\dot{8} = \frac{1}{55}$, write each of these as a fraction.
   a) 0·$\dot{0}3\dot{6}$
   b) 0·$\dot{0}5\dot{4}$
   c) 0·$\dot{3}0\dot{9}$

K KEY IDEAS

■ To multiply decimals, multiply the numbers ignoring the decimal points and then count the total number of decimal places in the two numbers. The answer will have this many decimal places.

■ To divide by a decimal with one decimal place, multiply both numbers by 10 (move the decimal point to the right one place) and then do the division.

■ Recurring decimals are written using the dot notation. For example

$0\cdot333\,333\,333... = 0\cdot\dot{3}$, $0\cdot342\,342\,342... = 0\cdot\dot{3}4\dot{2}$, $0\cdot018\,181\,818... = 0\cdot0\dot{1}\dot{8}$.

■ Terminating decimals are changed to fractions using the fraction that the last digit represents. For example, $0\cdot723 = \frac{723}{1000}$ because the digit '3' represents 3 thousandths.

Revision exercise D1

1 Write each of these as simply as possible.
  a) $\pi + \pi + \pi + \pi$
  b) $5\pi + 7\pi$
  c) $8^2\pi - 2^2\pi$
  d) $2 \times 17\pi$

2 Calculate these, leaving π in your answers.
  a) The circumference of a circle with radius 4 cm.
  b) The area of a circle with radius 13 cm.

3 A ring is made by removing a circle of radius 5 cm from a circle of radius 6 cm. What is the area of the ring? Leave π in your answer.

4 Look at this diagram.

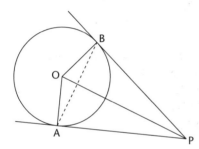

  a) If angle BPO is 32°, calculate
    (i) angle POB.
    (ii) angle OAB.
  b) If angle OAB is 25°, calculate angle APB.
  c) If angle ABP is 75°, calculate angle AOB.

5 Rearrange each formula to make the letter in brackets the subject.
  a) $x = y - 3b$ $\qquad$ (y)
  b) $t = \dfrac{u + v}{2}$ $\qquad$ (u)
  c) $P = 2b - a$ $\qquad$ (a)
  d) $p = qx + m$ $\qquad$ (q)
  e) $I = \dfrac{PTR}{100}$ $\qquad$ (P)
  f) $v^2 = u^2 + 2as$ $\qquad$ (s)

6 The sum $s°$ of the interior angles of a polygon with n sides is given by $s = 180(n - 2)$.
  a) Make n the subject of this formula.
  b) How many sides does a polygon have when the sum of its interior angles is 2880°?

7 Solve these equations.
  a) $3(x - 2) = x$
  b) $5(2x + 3) = 55$
  c) $4(x - 3) = 3(x - 2)$
  d) $2(3x - 4) = 4(x + 1)$

8 Solve these inequalities.
  a) $2x - 1 < 5$
  b) $3x + 4 \leqslant 16$
  c) $5x - 2 > 3 + 4x$
  d) $2(3x - 1) \leqslant 3x + 5$
  e) $2x - 3 < 3x - 1$
  f) $x + 2 > 3x + 1$
  g) $3(2x - 3) > 2(x - 5)$

9 An ice-lolly costs x pence and an ice-cream costs 20 pence more.
  a) Write down the cost of an ice-cream in terms of x.
  Jon buys three ice-lollies and two ice-creams and pays £3·40.
  b) Write down an equation in x and solve it to find the cost of an ice-lolly and the cost of an ice-cream.

10 Marcia is x cm tall and her friend Carole is 25 cm shorter.
  a) Write down Carole's height in terms of x.
  Their total height is 3 metres.
  b) Write down an equation in x and solve it to find Marcia's height.

11 Draw an angle of 65°. Construct the bisector of the angle.

STAG
7

12 Draw a line AB, 5 cm long.
Construct the perpendicular bisector of AB.

13 Draw a line 10 cm long. Mark a point anywhere above the line.
Construct the perpendicular from this point to the line.

14 Two points A and B are 6 cm apart.
Show, by shading, the locus of the points that are less than 5 cm from A and more than 5 cm from B.

15 Draw a rectangle ABCD with sides AB = 4 cm and BC = 3 cm.
Show the locus of the points outside the rectangle that are within 2 cm of the sides of the rectangle.

16 Draw a triangle ABC with AB = 8 cm, angle A = 47° and AC = 5 cm.
Show the locus of the points inside the triangle that are nearer to AB than AC.

17 This diagram shows the position of three schools.

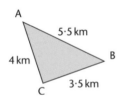

It is decided to build a swimming pool for the three schools. It must not be more than 3·5 km from any of the schools.
Using a scale of 2 cm : 1 km, make a scale drawing and show the region where the pool can be located.

18 Carterknowle church hall is rectangular with sides AB = 12 m and BC = 5 m. The main door is at corner C.
A spotlight is to be fixed on the ceiling, more than 6 m from the main door, more than 5 m from the opposite corner and nearer to AB than AD.
Using a scale of 1 cm : 1 m, make a scale drawing of the hall and show the region where the light can be fitted.

19 This is a plan of the floor area of a shop.

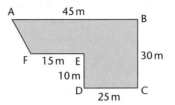

All the corners are 90° except A and F.
A heat detector is placed at A and another at D. They both have a range of 20 m and do not work round corners.
Using a scale of 1 cm : 5 m, make a scale drawing of the plan and show, by shading, the region that is not covered by the heat detectors.

20 This is a sketch of Sarah's patio.

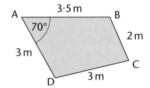

She wants to place a plant pot on the patio, within 1 m of AB, nearer to AB than AD, and no more than 2 m from A.
Using a scale of 2 cm : 1 m, make a scale drawing of the patio and show the region where the pot can be placed.

21 Work out these.
  a) 3 × 0·5
  b) 0·5 × 0·9
  c) 0·4 × 0·2
  d) 12 ÷ 0·2
  e) 69 ÷ 0·3
  f) 135 ÷ 0·5

22 Work out these.
  a) 6·4 × 2·5
  b) 111·7 × 3·85
  c) 8·45 × 0·91
  d) 12·9 ÷ 0·03
  e) 5·2452 ÷ 0·12
  f) 20·24 ÷ 1·15

23 Convert each of these fractions to a decimal. When the answer is a recurring decimal, use the dot notation.

a) $\frac{1}{8}$ **b)** $\frac{3}{11}$

c) $\frac{21}{125}$ **d)** $\frac{17}{33}$

e) $\frac{5}{32}$ **f)** $\frac{63}{132}$

24 Convert each of these decimals to a fraction in its lowest terms.

a) $0 \cdot 02$ **b)** $0 \cdot \dot{6}$

c) $0 \cdot 0\dot{6}$ **d)** $0 \cdot 72$

e) $0 \cdot 027$ **f)** $0 \cdot 1825$

STAG
7

Accuracy

You should already know

- How to round a number to the nearest whole number or a given number of decimal places
- How to convert one metric unit to another

Discrete and continuous measures

Discrete measures can be counted. They can only take particular values.

Continuous measures include length, time and mass. They cannot be measured exactly.

Look at this table of some data for a bicycle.

Number of wheels	2
Number of gears	15
Diameter of wheel	66 cm
Frame size	66 cm
Price	£99·99

In the table, the discrete measures are
- number of wheels
- number of gears
- price.

The continuous measures are
- diameter of wheel
- frame size.

EXERCISE 21.1

1 Look at these descriptions from catalogues.
Identify whether each data item is discrete or continuous.

   a) Prestige 20 cm polyester golf bag, 6-way graphite-friendly top, 2 accessory pockets

   b) Black attaché case, 2 folio compartments, 3 pen holders, size 3·15 cm (H), 44·5 cm (W), 11·5 cm (D)

   c) 16 piece dinner set, 4 dinner plates (diameter 24·5 cm), side plates and bowls

   d) Food blender, 1·5 litre working capacity, 3 speed settings, 400 watts

2 Read this extract from a newspaper article.

> Andy James has now scored 108 goals in just 167 games, making him the Town's most prolific scorer ever. In Saturday's game, a penalty brought his first goal after 30 minutes, with Pete Jeffreys having been fouled. *Six minutes* later, James volleyed into the net again, after a flick on from Neil Matty, *five yards* outside the penalty box.

   a) Give two examples of discrete data in the newspaper article.

   b) Give three examples of continuous data in the article.

3 Read this extract from a newspaper article.

> Lightning killed two people in Hyde Park yesterday as storms swept the south-east. *1·75 inches* of rain fell in *48 hours*. In Pagham winds of up to *120 mph* damaged more than *50 houses* and bungalows and several boats. One catamaran was flung *100 feet* into the air and landed in a tree.

   a) Give two examples of discrete data in the newspaper article.

   b) Give three examples of continuous data in the article.

4 Write a description which includes three discrete measurements and two continuous measurements.

Bounds of measurement

 A ACTIVITY 1

Write down three numbers which round to each of these.

   a) 26   **b)** 26·5   **c)** 43   **d)** 43·0   **e)** 50

Suppose a measurement is given as '26 cm to the nearest centimetre'. This means that the next possible measurements on either side are 25 cm and 27 cm. Where does the boundary between these measurements lie?

STAGE
7

Any measurement that is nearer to 26 cm than to 25 cm or 27 cm will be counted as 26 cm. This is the marked interval on the number line.

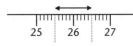

The boundaries of this interval are 25·5 cm and 26·5 cm. These values are exactly halfway between one measurement and the next. Usually when rounding to a given number of decimal places or significant figures, you would round 25·5 up to 26 and 26·5 up to 27.

So this gives
- The interval for 26 cm to the nearest centimetre is m cm where $25·5 \leqslant m < 26·5$.
- 25·5 cm is called the **lower bound** of the interval.
- 26·5 cm is called the **upper bound** of the interval (although it is not actually included in the interval).

EXAMPLE 1

Simon won the 200 m race in a time of 24·2 seconds to the nearest tenth of a second.

Complete the sentence below.

Simon's time was between … seconds and … seconds.

As the measurement is stated to the nearest tenth of a second, the next possible times are 24·1 seconds and 24·3 seconds.

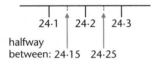

halfway
between: 24·15   24·25

Simon's time was between 24·15 seconds and 24·25 seconds.

EXERCISE 21.2

1 Give the upper and lower bounds of each of these measurements.

a) Given to the nearest centimetre
- **(i)** 27 cm
- **(ii)** 30 cm
- **(iii)** 128 cm

b) Given to the nearest 10 cm
- **(i)** 10 cm
- **(ii)** 30 cm
- **(iii)** 150 cm

c) Given to the nearest millimetre
- **(i)** 5·6 cm
- **(ii)** 0·8 cm
- **(iii)** 12·0 cm

d) Given to the nearest centimetre
- **(i)** 1·23 m
- **(ii)** 0·45 m
- **(iii)** 9·08 m

e) Given to the nearest hundredth of a second
- **(i)** 10·62 seconds
- **(ii)** 9·81 seconds
- **(iii)** 48·10 seconds

f) Given to the nearest centimetre
- **(i)** 34 cm
- **(ii)** 92 cm
- **(iii)** 210 cm

EXERCISE 21.2 continued

g) Given to the nearest 10 cm
- **(i)** 20 cm
- **(ii)** 60 cm
- **(iii)** 210 cm

h) Given to the nearest millimetre
- **(i)** 2·7 cm
- **(ii)** 0·2 cm
- **(iii)** 18·0 cm

i) Given to the nearest centimetre
- **(i)** 8·17 m
- **(ii)** 0·36 m
- **(iii)** 2·04 m

j) Given to the nearest hundredth of a second
- **(i)** 15·61 seconds
- **(ii)** 12·10 seconds
- **(iii)** 54·07 seconds

2 Complete each of these sentences.

a) A mass given as 57 kg to the nearest kilogram is between … kg and … kg.

b) A height given as 4·7 m to 1 decimal place is between … m and … m.

c) A volume given as 468 ml to the nearest millilitre is between … ml and … ml.

d) A winning time given as 34·91 seconds to the nearest hundredth of a second is between … seconds and … seconds.

e) A mass given as 0·634 kg to the nearest gram is between … kg and … kg.

f) A mass given as 64 kg to the nearest kilogram is between … kg and … kg.

g) A height given as 8·3 m to 1 decimal place is between … m and … m.

h) A volume given as 234 ml to the nearest millilitre is between … ml and … ml.

i) A winning time given as 27·94 seconds to the nearest hundredth of a second is between … seconds and … seconds.

j) A mass given as 0·256 kg to the nearest gram is between … kg and … kg.

CHALLENGE 1

A chimneysweep uses a pole made up of ten identical flexible pieces.
Each piece is 1 metre long, measured to the nearest centimetre.

What height of chimney can you be sure that he could reach?

CHALLENGE 2

Emma measures her pencil to be 18 cm and her pencil case states a length of 18·5 cm.

Can Emma be sure that her pencil will fit inside the pencil case? Explain your answer.

C CHALLENGE 3

A rectangle measures 12 cm by 5 cm, with both measurements correct to the nearest centimetre.

a) Work out the greatest possible perimeter of the rectangle.

b) Work out the smallest possible area of the rectangle.

K KEY IDEAS

- Discrete measures can be counted. They can only take particular values.

- Continuous measures include length, time, mass, and so on. They cannot be measured exactly.

- A time of 5·7 seconds to the nearest tenth of a second lies between 5·65 seconds and 5·75 seconds.

Indices

You will learn about

- Simplifying expressions using powers
- The three basic rules for combining indices
- Calculating proficiently with squares, cubes, square roots and cube roots

You should already know

- The meaning of the terms *square number* and *cube number*
- The meaning of a power such as 2^2 and 2^3

Indices (or **powers**) are a form of mathematical shorthand.

$3 \times 3 \times 3 \times 3$ is written as 3^4 and

$2 \times 2 \times 2 \times 2 \times 2 \times 2 \times 2 \times 2$ is written as 2^8.

A   ACTIVITY 1

$2^2 \times 2^5 = (2 \times 2) \times (2 \times 2 \times 2 \times 2 \times 2) = 2^7$.

By writing the powers out fully as above, find each missing index indicated with a question mark.

a) $2^3 \times 2^2 = 2^?$ **b)** $2^4 \times 2^5 = 2^?$ **c)** $3^6 \div 3^4 = 3^?$

d) $4^8 \div 4^3 = 4^?$ **e)** $(3^3)^2 = 3^?$

STAGE
7

22

Multiplying numbers in index form

$3^4 \times 3^8 = (3 \times 3 \times 3 \times 3) \times (3 \times 3 \times 3 \times 3 \times 3 \times 3 \times 3 \times 3)$
$\qquad = 3 \times 3 \times 3 \times 3 \times 3 \times 3 \times 3 \times 3 \times 3 \times 3 \times 3 \times 3$
$\qquad = 3^{12}$

The indices are added:
$3^4 \times 3^8 = 3^{4+8}$
$\qquad = 3^{12}$

The rule is $n^a \times n^b = n^{a+b}$

Dividing numbers in index form

$2^6 \div 2^4 = \dfrac{\cancel{2} \times \cancel{2} \times \cancel{2} \times \cancel{2} \times 2 \times 2}{\cancel{2} \times \cancel{2} \times \cancel{2} \times \cancel{2}}$
$\qquad = 2 \times 2$
$\qquad = 2^2$

The indices are subtracted: $2^6 \div 2^4 = 2^{6-4}$
$\qquad\qquad\qquad\qquad\qquad = 2^2$

The rule is $n^a \div n^b = n^{a-b}$

EXAMPLE 1

Write these in index form.

a) $5 \times 5 \times 6 \times 6 \times 6 \times 6$

b) $3x^3 \times 4x^5$

c) $25x^4 \div 5x^2$

a) $5 \times 5 \times 6 \times 6 \times 6 \times 6 = 5^2 \times 6^4$

b) $3x^3 \times 4x^5 = 12x^8$

c) $25x^4 \div 5x^2 = \dfrac{25x^4}{5x^2} = 5x^2$

STAGE
7

EXERCISE 22.1

1 Write these in a simpler form, using indices.
   a) $3 \times 3 \times 3 \times 3 \times 3$
   b) $7 \times 7 \times 7$
   c) $8 \times 8 \times 8 \times 8 \times 8$
   d) $4 \times 4 \times 4 \times 4 \times 4$
   e) $8 \times 8 \times 8$
   f) $2 \times 2 \times 2 \times 2 \times 2$

2 Write these in a simpler form, using indices.
   a) $5 \times 4 \times 4 \times 4 \times 5$
   b) $3 \times 3 \times 5 \times 5 \times 5$
   c) $2 \times 2 \times 2 \times 3 \times 3 \times 4 \times 4 \times 4 \times 4 \times 4$
   d) $7 \times 7 \times 7 \times 8 \times 8 \times 9 \times 9 \times 9$

3 Write these in a simpler form, using indices.
   a) $5^2 \times 5^3$ **b)** $6^2 \times 6^7$
   c) $10^3 \times 10^4$ **d)** $3^6 \times 3^5$
   e) $8^3 \times 8^2$ **f)** $4^2 \times 4^3$
   g) $9^2 \times 9^7$ **h)** $6^2 \times 6^6$

4 Write these in a simpler form, using indices.
   a) $10^5 \div 10^2$ **b)** $3^5 \div 3^2$
   c) $8^4 \div 8^2$ **d)** $7^5 \div 7^3$
   e) $6^3 \div 6^2$

5 Work out these, giving your answers in index form.
   a) $\dfrac{3^9}{3^5 \times 3^2}$ **b)** $\dfrac{2^4 \times 2^3}{2^5}$

   c) $\dfrac{5^4 \times 5^5}{5^2 \times 5^3}$ **d)** $\dfrac{4^{12}}{4^5 \times 4^4}$

   e) $\dfrac{2^5 \times 2^6}{2^4}$ **f)** $\dfrac{6^5 \times 6^4}{6^2 \times 6}$

7 Write these as a single power of a.
   a) $a^2 \times a^3$ **b)** $a^4 \times a^5$
   c) $a^4 \times a^2$ **d)** $a^3 \times a^6$

8 Write these as a single power of a.
   a) $a^6 \div a^4$ **b)** $a^7 \div a^3$
   c) $a^8 \div a^2$ **d)** $a^5 \div a^2$

9 Simplify these.
   a) $2a^2 \times 3a^3$ **b)** $4a^4 \times 3a^5$
   c) $3a^4 \times 4a^2$ **d)** $5a^3 \times 3a^6$

10 Simplify these.
   a) $6a^6 \div 2a^4$ **b)** $10a^7 \div 5a^3$
   c) $6a^8 \div 3a^2$ **d)** $12a^5 \div 4a^2$

C   CHALLENGE 1

a) Simplify these as much as possible.

   (i) $(x)^2$ **(ii)** $(3^4)^2$ **(iii)** $(a^3)^5$ **(iv)** $(2y^2)^3$ **(v)** $(3x^3)^4$

b) Use your answers to part **a)** to complete statements 2 and 3.

   1 Powers of numbers and letters can also be raised to powers.

   2 If the numbers and letters are in brackets, the indices are …

   3 The rule is $(n^a)^b = \ldots$

Powers and roots

The set of numbers 1, 4, 9, 16, 25, 36, 49, 64, 81, 100, 121, 144, 169, 196, 225, ... are the **square numbers**.

Each of them can be written as the square of a counting number as shown in the table.

Number	1	4	9	16	25	36	49	64	81	100	121	144	169	196	225
Square	1^2	2^2	3^2	4^2	5^2	6^2	7^2	8^2	9^2	10^2	11^2	12^2	13^2	14^2	15^2

Because $16 = 4^2$, the 'square root' of 16 is 4. This is written as $\sqrt{16} = 4$.

Similarly, $\sqrt{36} = 6$ and $\sqrt{81} = 9$.

But $(^-4)^2 = 16$ as well as $4^2 = 16$. It follows that the square root of 16 could be 4 or $^-4$. This is often written ±4.

Similarly, the square root of $81 = \pm9$.

> **EXAM TIP**
> You are expected to know the squares up to $15^2 = 225$, so you should learn these.

> **EXAM TIP**
> In many practical problems where the answers are square roots, the negative answer would not have a meaning and so it should be left out.

The numbers 1, 8, 27, 64, 125, ..., 1000, ... are **cube numbers** because each of them can be written as the cube of a whole number.

Number	1	8	27	64	125	...	1000	...
Cube	1^3	2^3	3^3	4^3	5^3	...	10^3	...

> **EXAM TIP**
> The cube numbers shown are the ones you are expected to remember and so you should learn them.

Because $27 = 3^3$, the cube root of 27 is 3. This is written as $\sqrt[3]{27} = 3$.

You may get easy square roots and cube roots in the non-calculator section of an examination paper, but make sure you can find and use the $\boxed{\sqrt[3]{\ }}$ and $\boxed{\sqrt{\ }}$ buttons on your calculator.

On older calculators, you may have to put the number in first and then press the correct button. On most modern calculators, you press the root button first, then the number, then $\boxed{=}$.

So $\boxed{\sqrt{\ }}$ $\boxed{5}$ $\boxed{2}$ $\boxed{=}$ 7·211...

STAGE
7

Indices

EXERCISE 22.2

 Do not use your calculator for questions **1** to **7**.

1 Write down the square of each number.
a) 7   b) 12
c) 8   d) 11
e) $\sqrt{10}$

2 Write down the square root of each number.
a) 36   b) 81
c) 169   d) 196
e) 23^2

3 Write down the cube of each number.
a) 4   b) 5
c) 3   d) 10
e) $\sqrt[3]{18}$

4 Write down the cube root of each number.
a) 8   b) 1
c) 64   d) 1000
e) 20^3

5 Find the area of a square of side 4 mm.

6 Solve the equation $x^2 = 81$.

7 a) Which number is $3^2 \times 4^2$?
b) Write 36 as a product of prime factors.

 You may use your calculator for questions **8** to **16**.

8 Write down the square of each number.
a) 25   b) 40
c) 35   d) 50
e) 73

9 Write down the square root of each number.
a) 400   b) 289
c) 361   d) 10 000
e) 7921

10 Write down the cube of each number.
a) 7   b) 9
c) 20   d) 25
e) 1·5   f) 2·7
g) 5·4

11 Write down the cube root of each number.
a) 343   b) 729
c) 1331   d) 1 000 000
e) 216   f) 1728
g) 512

12 Work these out.
Give your answers to 2 decimal places.
a) $\sqrt{56}$ b) $\sqrt{27}$
c) $\sqrt{60}$ d) $\sqrt{70}$
e) $\sqrt{39}$ f) $\sqrt{90}$
g) $\sqrt{280}$ h) $\sqrt{678}$
i) $\sqrt{380}$ j) $\sqrt{456}$

13 Find the length of a square of area 14 cm².
Give your answer to 2 decimal places.

14 Find the length of a cube whose volume is 45 cm³.
Give your answer to 2 decimal places.

15 Put these numbers in order, smallest first.
2^3, 3^2, 4^2, $\sqrt{25}$, $\sqrt[3]{343}$, 5^2

16 Find $\left(\sqrt[3]{16}\right)^3$. You should be able to do it without a calculator. If you could not, try it with a calculator. What do you notice?

STAGE

7

C **CHALLENGE 2**

I think of a number, I find its cube root and then square that. The answer is 9.

What is the number I thought of?

C **CHALLENGE 3**

Find two numbers less than 200 which are both square numbers and cube numbers.

K **KEY IDEAS**

■ To multiply using powers, use the rule $n^a \times n^b = n^{a+b}$.

■ To divide using powers, use the rule $n^a \div n^b = n^{a-b}$.

■ You should know the squares from 1^2 to 15^2.

■ You should know the values of 1^3, 2^3, 3^3, 4^3, 5^3 and 10^3.

■ You should know how to find and use the square root and cube root buttons on your calculator.

Trial and improvement

You will learn about

- Finding consecutive integers between which the solution of an equation lies
- Using the method of trial and improvement to solve an equation to a given degree of accuracy

You should already know

- How to substitute numbers into algebraic expressions

A ACTIVITY 1

A cuboid has a square base. The height of the cuboid is 2 cm more than the sides of the base, and the volume of the cuboid is 500 cm³.

Find the dimensions of the cuboid, correct to 2 decimal places. Use the table below to help you.

Length (cm)	Width (cm)	Height (cm)	Volume (cm³)
5	5	7	5 × 5 × 7 = 175
10	10	12	
7	7	9	

The activity is an example of using trial and improvement to find the solution to a problem. The numbers are changed systematically to get as close as possible to the target value of 500. We start off by trialling whole numbers and then move on to decimal numbers to get closer to the target value.

STAGE

7

189

Solving cubic equations by trial and improvement

Often you are told that the solution of an equation lies between two given numbers. If you are not told this, your first step must be to find these two values. Then choose the number halfway between these values. Keep making improvements until the required accuracy is achieved.

EXAMPLE 1

A solution of the equation $x^3 - 4x + 1 = 0$ lies between 1 and 2.

Use trial and improvement to find the solution correct to 1 decimal place.

You have been given two values between which the solution lies, so for the first trial use the value halfway between these, that is 1·5. A table can be used to set out your trials.

x-value	Calculation	Comment
1·5	$1·5^3 - 4 \times 1·5 + 1 = {}^-1·625$	Too small, so try a value between 1·5 and 2·0
1·8	$1·8^3 - 4 \times 1·8 + 1 = {}^-0·368$	Too small, so try a value between 1·8 and 2·0
1·9	$1·9^3 - 4 \times 1·9 + 1 = 0·259$	Too big, so the solution lies between 1·8 and 1·9
1·85	$1·85^3 - 4 \times 1·85 + 1 = {}^-0·0684$	Too small, so the solution lies between 1·85 and 1·9

The solution is greater than 1·85 so is nearer to 1·9 than to 1·8.

It is $x = 1·9$, correct to 1 decimal place.

EXAM TIP

Make sure you give the *x*-value (not the value on the right-hand side of the equation) to the required accuracy.

EXAMPLE 2

Show that $x^3 - 3x = 6$ has a solution between 2 and 3.

Find the solution correct to 1 decimal place.

$2^3 - 3 \times 2 = 2$
$3^3 - 3 \times 3 = 18$

Because 6 is between 2 and 18, there is a solution for x between 2 and 3.
For the first trial use the value halfway between these, that is 2·5.

x-value	Calculation	Comment
2·5	$2.5^3 - 3 \times 2.5 = 8.125$	Too big, so try a value between 2 and 2·5
2·3	$2.3^3 - 3 \times 2.3 = 5.267$	Too small, so try a value between 2·3 and 2·5
2·4	$2.4^3 - 3 \times 2.4 = 6.624$	Too big, so the solution lies between 2·3 and 2·4
2·35	$2.35^3 - 3 \times 2.35 = 5.928$	Too small, so the solution lies between 2·35 and 2·4

The solution is nearer to 2·4 than to 2·3.

It is $x = 2.4$, correct to 1 decimal place.

EXAM TIP

Always give the result of the calculation for the trial you have done as well as saying 'too big' or 'too small'.

EXERCISE 23.1

Use trial and improvement to find the solutions.

1 a) $1^3 = 1$ and $2^3 = 8$.
Explain how this shows that there is a solution to the equation $x^3 = 5$ between 1 and 2.

b) Find the solution correct to 1 decimal place.

2 a) $2^3 - 8 \times 2 = ^-8$ and $3^3 - 8 \times 3 = 3$.
Explain how this shows that there is a solution to the equation $x^3 - 8x = 0$ between 2 and 3.

b) Find the solution correct to 1 decimal place.

3 a) $2^3 = 8$ and $3^3 = 27$.
Explain how this shows that there is a solution to the equation $x^3 = 15$ between 2 and 3.

b) Find the solution correct to 1 decimal place.

4 a) $1^3 - 2 \times 1 = ^-1$ and $2^3 - 2 \times 2 = 4$.
Explain how this shows that there is a solution to the equation $x^3 - 2x = 0$ between 1 and 2.

b) Find the solution correct to 1 decimal place.

STAGE
7

EXERCISE 23.1 continued

5 Show that a solution of $x^3 - 5x = 8$ lies between 2 and 3.
Find it correct to 1 decimal place.

6 Show that a solution of $x^3 - x = 90$ lies between 4 and 5.
Find it correct to 1 decimal place.

7 Show that a solution of $x^3 - x^2 = 30$ lies between 3 and 4.
Find it correct to 1 decimal place.

8 Show that a solution of $x^3 - 7x = 25$ lies between 3 and 4.
Find it correct to 1 decimal place.

9 Show that a solution of $x^3 + 2x = 2$ lies between 0 and 1.
Find it correct to 1 decimal place.

10 Show that a solution of $x^3 - x^2 = 1$ lies between 1 and 2.
Find it correct to 1 decimal place.

11 A solution of $x^3 = 12$ lies between 2 and 3.
Find it correct to 2 decimal places.

12 A solution of $x^3 + 50 = 0$ lies between ⁻4 and ⁻3.
Find it correct to 1 decimal place.

13 A solution of $x^3 + 4x + 25 = 0$ lies between ⁻3 and ⁻2.
Find it correct to 1 decimal place.

14 A solution of $x^3 = 56$ lies between 3 and 4.
Find it correct to 2 decimal places.

15 A solution of $x^3 + 12 = 0$ lies between ⁻3 and ⁻2.
Find it correct to 1 decimal place.

16 A solution of $x^3 - 2x + 6 = 0$ lies between ⁻3 and ⁻2.
Find it correct to 1 decimal place.

17 **a)** Find two consecutive integers between which the solution of $x^3 - 2x^2 = 4$ lies.
b) Find the solution correct to 2 decimal places.

18 A solution of $x^3 + 3x^2 + x = 0$ lies between ⁻3 and ⁻2.
Find it correct to 2 decimal places.

19 **a)** Find two consecutive integers between which a solution of $x^3 + 3x - 20 = 0$ lies.
b) Find the solution correct to 2 decimal places.

20 A solution of $x^3 - 5x^2 + 2x = 0$ lies between 0 and 1.
Find it correct to 2 decimal places.

STAGE
7

KEY IDEAS

- To find the solution to an equation by trial and improvement, first find two consecutive numbers that the solution lies between. Then choose the number halfway between these values. Keep making improvements until the required accuracy is achieved.

Sequences 24

You will learn about

- Recognising a linear sequence
- Using the formula for the *n*th term of a sequence
- Finding the formula for the *n*th term of a linear sequence

You should already know

- The sets of square and cube numbers

Linear sequences

Look at this sequence.

2, 5, 8, 11, 14, ...

The terms of the sequence increase by 3 every time. When the increase is constant like this, the sequence is called a **linear** sequence.

In the same way, the sequence 11, 9, 7, 5, 3, 1, ⁻1, ... is also linear, since the terms decrease by the same amount (2) every time. Another way of thinking of this is that you are adding ⁻2 each time. This idea will help with finding the *n*th term.

C CHALLENGE 1

Work in pairs.

Each of you find as many different sequences as you can where the first two terms are 1 and 3. For each sequence, write down the first four terms on a separate piece of paper. On the back of the paper, write the rule you have used.

Swap a sequence with your partner.

Try to find each other's rule.

EXERCISE 24.1

Which of these sequences are linear and which are not? For each sequence, write down the next two terms.

1 3   5   7   9

2 43   40   38   35

3 78   75   72   69

4 1   5   9   13

5 4   9   16   25

6 1   6   15   28

7 2   9   16   23

The nth term

It is often possible to find a formula to give the terms of a sequence.

You usually use n to stand for the number of a term.

EXAMPLE 1

The formula is nth term $= 2n + 1$. Find each of these terms.

a) 1st term   **b)** 2nd term   **c)** 3rd term

a) The 1st term $= 2 \times 1 + 1 = 3$

b) The 2nd term $= 2 \times 2 + 1 = 5$

c) The 3rd term $= 2 \times 3 + 1 = 7$

EXERCISE 24.2

Each of these is the formula for the nth term of a sequence.
Find the first four terms of each sequence.

1   $n + 1$

2   $2n$

3   $2n - 1$

4   $n + 5$

5   $3n$

6   $3n + 1$

7   $5n - 3$

8   $10n$

9   $7n - 7$

10   $2 - n$

11   n

12   $n + 3$

13   $4n$

14   $n - 1$

15   $2n + 1$

16   $3n - 1$

17   $6n + 5$

18   $2n - 3$

19   $5 - n$

20   $10 - 2n$

 CHALLENGE 2

Each of these is the formula for the nth term of a sequence.
Find the first four terms of each sequence.

a) n^2 **b)** $n^2 + 2$ **c)** $n^2 - 5$ **d)** $3n^2$ **e)** n^3

Finding the formula for the nth term

Look back at the formulae in Exercise 24.2 and the sequences in your answers, and notice how
they are connected. If the formula contains a '$2n$', the terms increase by 2 each time; if it contains
a '$5n$', the terms increase by 5 each time. Similarly, if it contains '$-3n$' it increases by -3 (or goes
down 3) each time. So to find a formula for a given sequence, find how much more (or less) each
term is than the one before it.

STAGE

7

> **EXAM TIP**
> This will always work if
> the differences are the
> same each time.

EXAMPLE 2

Find the formula for the *n*th term of this sequence.

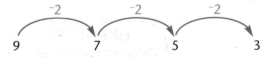

The differences between all the terms are 2, so the formula will include a '2*n*'.

When *n* = 1, 2*n* = 2.

But the first term of the sequence is 3, which is 1 more.

The formula will be *n*th term = 2*n* + 1.

EXAMPLE 3

Find the formula for the *n*th term of this sequence.

<pre>
    ⁻2   ⁻2   ⁻2
9   7   5   3
</pre>

The differences here are still 2 but they must be ⁻2, as the terms are getting smaller.

This time the formula will include a '⁻2*n*', to make the terms get smaller.

When *n* = 1, ⁻2*n* = ⁻2.

But the first term of the sequence is 9, which is 11 more.

The formula for the *n*th term is ⁻2*n* + 11, or 11 − 2*n*.

STAGE
7

EXERCISE 24.3

Find the formula for the *n*th term for each of these sequences.

1	1	2	3	4		**11**	2	5	8	11
2	4	6	8	10		**12**	7	9	11	13
3	4	8	12	16		**13**	4	9	14	19
4	0	2	4	6		**14**	15	20	25	30
5	7	11	15	19		**15**	⁻1	3	7	11
6	1	7	13	19		**16**	5	7	9	11
7	11	21	31	41		**17**	101	102	103	104
8	5	8	11	14		**18**	4	3	2	1
9	101	201	301	401		**19**	7	4	1	⁻2
10	0	1	2	3		**20**	25	23	21	19

EXAM TIP

Check that your formula for the *n*th term is correct by trying it out for the first few terms. Put *n* = 1, 2, 3, ...

 KEY IDEAS

- If the differences between the terms of a sequence are all the same, the sequence is linear.

- If this difference is *a*, the formula for the *n*th term of the sequence will be *an* + *b*. Put in a value of *n* to find the value of *b*.

STAGE

7

Multiplying out two brackets

You should already know

- How to collect together simple algebraic terms
- How to expand single brackets

You might remember that expressions such as $a(3a - 2b)$ can be multiplied out to give

$$a(3a - 2b) = (a \times 3a) - (a \times 2b)$$
$$= 3a^2 - 2ab.$$

When multiplying out two pairs of brackets you must multiply each term inside the second bracket by each term inside the first bracket. The examples which follow show three methods for doing this.

EXAM TIP

Choose the method you prefer and stick to it.

EXAMPLE 1

Expand these.

a) $(a + 2)(a + 5)$ **b)** $(b + 4)(b - 1)$ **c)** $(m - 5)(m - 4)$

a) Method 1
Expand the first bracket and then multiply out.

$$(a + 2)(a + 5) = a(a + 5) + 2(a + 5)$$
$$= a^2 + 5a + 2a + 10$$
$$= a^2 + 7a + 10$$

Notice that the middle two terms are **like terms** and so can be collected.

EXAM TIP

You may be asked to multiply out, simplify, expand or remove the brackets. These all mean the same.

STAGE 7

EXAMPLE 1 continued

25

Multiplying out two brackets

Method 2
Use a grid to multiply each of the terms in the
second bracket by each of the terms in the first.

x	a	+2
a	a^2	+2a
+5	+5a	+10

$= a^2 + 2a + 5a + 10$
$= a^2 + 7a + 10$

Method 3
Use the word FOIL to make sure you multiply each
term in the second bracket by each term in the first.

F: first × first
O: outer × outer
I: inner × inner
L: last × last

If you draw arrows to show the multiplications,
you can think of a smiley face.

$(a + 5)(a + 2) = a \times a + a \times 2 + a \times 5 + 5 \times 2$
$\qquad\qquad\qquad = a^2 + 2a + 5a + 10$
$\qquad\qquad\qquad = a^2 + 7a + 10$

b) Method 1
$(b + 4)(b - 1) = b(b - 1) + 4(b - 1)$
$\qquad\qquad\qquad = b^2 - b + 4b - 4$
$\qquad\qquad\qquad = b^2 + 3b - 4$

Method 2

x	b	+4
b	b^2	+4b
-1	-1b	-4

$= b^2 + 4b - 1b - 4$
$= b^2 + 3b - 4$

Method 3

$(b + 4)(b - 1) = b \times b + b \times {}^-1 + 4 \times b + 4 \times {}^-1$
$\qquad\qquad\qquad = b^2 - 1b + 4b - 4$
$\qquad\qquad\qquad = b^2 + 3b - 4$

EXAM TIP
Most errors are made in
multiplying out the second
bracket when the sign in
front is negative.

c) Method 1
$(m - 5)(m - 4) = m(m - 4) - 5(m - 4)$
$\qquad\qquad\qquad = m^2 - 4m - 5m + 20$
$\qquad\qquad\qquad = m^2 - 9m + 20$

Method 2

x	m	-5
m	m^2	-5m
-4	-4m	+20

$= m^2 - 5m - 4m + 20$
$= m^2 - 9m + 20$

Method 3

$(m - 5)(m - 4) = m \times m + m \times {}^-4 - 5 \times m - 5 \times {}^-4$
$\qquad\qquad\qquad = m^2 - 4m - 5m + 20$
$\qquad\qquad\qquad = m^2 - 9m + 20$

STAGE
7

There are two special types of expansions of two brackets that you need to know.

The first is when a bracket is squared, as in parts **a)** and **b)** of the next example. The important thing with this type of expansion is to make sure that you write the brackets separately and that you end up with three terms.

The second type is shown in part **c)** of the example. With this type of expansion, you get only two terms because the middle terms cancel each other out. This type is known as the **difference of two squares** because $(A - B)(A + B) = A^2 - B^2$.

▍▍ EXAMPLE 2

Expand these brackets.

a) $(x + 3)^2$ **b)** $(x - 3)^2$ **c)** $(x + 3)(x - 3)$

$$\begin{aligned}
\textbf{a)} \quad (x + 3)^2 &= (x + 3)(x + 3) \\
&= x(x + 3) + 3(x + 3) \\
&= x^2 + 3x + 3x + 9 \\
&= x^2 + 6x + 9
\end{aligned}$$

The method shown is method 1 but you can use any of the methods shown in Example 1. You will get the same answer.

$$\begin{aligned}
\textbf{b)} \quad (x - 3)^2 &= (x - 3)(x - 3) \\
&= x(x - 3) - 3(x - 3) \\
&= x^2 - 3x - 3x + 9 \\
&= x^2 - 6x + 9
\end{aligned}$$

$$\begin{aligned}
\textbf{c)} \quad (x + 3)(x - 3) &= x(x - 3) + 3(x - 3) \\
&= x^2 - 3x + 3x - 9 \\
&= x^2 - 9
\end{aligned}$$

EXAM TIP
Take care with the negative signs.

▍▍ EXERCISE 25.1

Multiply out the brackets.

1 $(x + 2)(x + 3)$ **7** $(x - 3)(x + 6)$

2 $(a + 4)(a + 3)$ **8** $(x - 5)(x - 4)$

3 $(a + 2)(a + 1)$ **9** $(x + 1)(x + 3)$

4 $(x + 5)(x - 2)$ **10** $(a + 3)(a + 3)$

5 $(x + 7)(x - 3)$ **11** $(a + 2)(a + 1)$

6 $(x - 5)(x - 6)$ **12** $(x - 2)(x + 1)$

STAGE 7

EXERCISE 25.1 continued

13 $(p + 4)(p - 2)$

14 $(a + 7)(a + 8)$

15 $(x - 6)(x + 4)$

16 $(x - 9)(x - 3)$

17 $(x + 10)(x - 1)$

18 $(x + 3)^2$

19 $(a - 5)^2$

20 $(b + 1)^2$

21 $(x - 2)^2$

22 $(a + 2)^2$

23 $(x - 10)^2$

24 $(x + 8)^2$

25 $(b - 7)^2$

26 $(x + 2)(x - 2)$

27 $(x + 6)(x - 6)$

28 $(x - 4)(x + 4)$

29 $(x + 1)(x - 1)$

30 $(x + 10)(x - 10)$

31 $(x + 4)^2$

32 $(x + 7)(x - 7)$

C CHALLENGE 1

Multiply out the brackets.

a) $(x + 2)(2x + 1)$　　**b)** $(2x + 3)(x - 2)$　　**c)** $(5y - 2)(2y + 1)$

d) $(2x + y)(2x - y)$　　**e)** $(6x - y)(3x - 2y)$

K KEY IDEAS

■ When multiplying out two brackets, multiply every term in the first bracket by every term in the second.

■ $(A - B)(A + B) = A^2 - B^2$ is called the difference of two squares.

STAGE
7

Prisms and units

You will learn about

- Finding the volume of a prism, in particular the volume of a cylinder
- Solving problems involving the volume of a prism
- Finding the surface area of a prism, in particular the surface area of a cylinder
- Converting between metric units of area and volume

You should already know

- Common metric units for length, area and volume
- How to find the area of a rectangle, triangle, parallelogram and trapezium
- How to find the circumference and area of a circle
- How to find lengths using Pythagoras' theorem
- How to round answers to a suitable degree of accuracy

The volume of a prism

A **prism** is a three-dimensional shape that has the same cross-section throughout its length.

A **cuboid** is a prism with a rectangular cross-section.

You should remember how to find the volume of a cuboid.

**STAGE
7**

| **Volume of a cuboid = length × width × height** |

You can also think of this as

| **Volume of a cuboid = area of cross-section × height** |

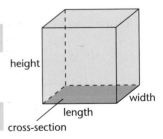

This is an example of a general formula for the volume of a prism. When laid on its side, along its length,

Volume of a prism = area of cross-section × length

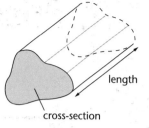

length

cross-section

Another important prism is the **cylinder**. Its cross-section is a circle, which has area πr^2.

Volume of a cylinder = $\pi r^2 h$

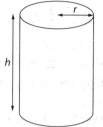 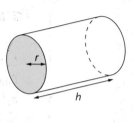

EXAMPLE 1

Calculate the volume of a cylinder with base diameter 15 cm and height 10 cm.

Radius of base $\frac{15}{2}$ = 7·5 cm

$$\begin{aligned}
\text{Volume of a cylinder} &= \pi r^2 h \\
&= \pi \times 7{\cdot}5^2 \times 10 \\
&= 1767 \text{ cm}^3, \text{ to the nearest whole number.}
\end{aligned}$$

EXAMPLE 2

A chocolate box is a prism with a trapezium as cross-section, as shown.

Calculate the volume of the prism.

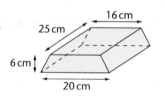

25 cm   16 cm

6 cm   20 cm

$$\begin{aligned}
\text{Area of a trapezium} &= \tfrac{1}{2}(a + b)h \\
&= \tfrac{1}{2}(20 + 16) \times 6 \\
&= 108 \text{ cm}^2
\end{aligned}$$

$$\begin{aligned}
\text{Volume of a prism} &= \text{area of cross-section} \times \text{length} \\
&= 108 \times 25 \\
&= 2700 \text{ cm}^3
\end{aligned}$$

STAGE

7

EXAMPLE 3

A cylinder has volume 100 cm³ and is 4·2 cm high.

Find the radius of its base. Give your answer to the nearest millimetre.

Volume of a cylinder = $\pi r^2 h$

$$100 = \pi \times r^2 \times 4{\cdot}2$$

$$r^2 = \frac{100}{\pi \times 4{\cdot}2}$$

$$= 7{\cdot}578\ldots$$

$$r = \sqrt{7{\cdot}578}\ldots$$

$$= 2{\cdot}752\ldots$$

$$= 2{\cdot}8\,\text{cm, to the nearest millimetre.}$$

EXERCISE 26.1

1 Calculate the volume of a cylinder with base radius 5·6 cm and height 8·5 cm.

2 A cylindrical stick of rock is 12 cm long and has radius 2·4 cm.
Find its volume.

3 A cylinder has diameter 8 cm and height 8 cm.
Calculate its volume.

4 Calculate the volume of a prism 15 cm long with each of these cross-sections.

a)
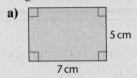
5 cm
7 cm

b)
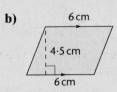
6 cm
4·5 cm
6 cm

c)
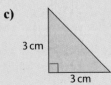
3 cm
3 cm

5 A chocolate bar is in the shape of a triangular prism.
Calculate its volume.

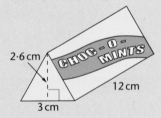
2·6 cm
CHOC-O-MINTS
12 cm
3 cm

6 Calculate the volume of a cylinder with base radius 4·3 cm and height 9·7 cm.

7 A cylindrical water tank is 4·2 m high and has radius 3·6 m.
Find its volume.

8 A cylinder has diameter 9 cm and height 12 cm.
Calculate its volume.

9 Calculate the volume of a prism 12 cm long with each of these cross-sections.

a)

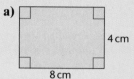

b)

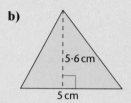

c)

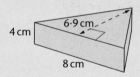

10 A gift box is a prism with a triangular base.
Calculate its volume.

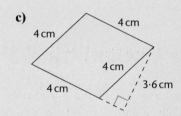

11 A pencil-box is a prism with a trapezium as its cross-section, as shown.
Calculate the volume of the box.

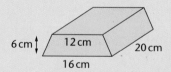

12 The area of cross-section of a prism is 75 cm². Its volume is 1200 cm³.
Calculate its length.

13 The volume of a cylinder is 800 cm³.
Its radius is 5·3 cm.
Calculate its height.

14 A cylinder has volume 570 cm³ and height 7 cm.
Find its base radius. Give your answer to the nearest millimetre.

15 The volume of a cylindrical tank is 600 m³. Its height is 4·6 m.
Calculate the radius of its base.

16 A vase is a prism with a trapezium as its base. The internal measurements are as shown.

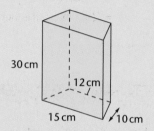

How much water can the vase hold?
Give your answer in litres.
(1 litre = 1000 cm³)

17 The area of cross-section of a prism is 90 cm². Its volume is 1503 cm³.
Calculate its length.

18 The volume of a cylinder is 1500 cm³.
Its radius is 7·5 cm.
Calculate its height. Give your answer to the nearest millimetre.

19 A cylinder has volume 620 cm³ and height 8 cm.
Find its base radius. Give your answer to the nearest millimetre.

20 The volume of a cylinder is 1100 cm³.
Its height is 10·8 cm.
Calculate its radius. Give your answer to the nearest millimetre.

STAGE

7

26

The surface area of a prism

To find the total surface area of a prism, simply add up the surface area of all the individual surfaces.

▌▌ EXAMPLE 4

Find the total surface area of this prism.

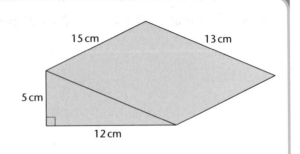

Area of end $= \frac{1}{2} \times 12 \times 5 = 30\,\text{cm}^2$
Area of other end $\qquad\quad = 30\,\text{cm}^2$
Area of base $= 12 \times 15 \quad = 180\,\text{cm}^2$
Area of top $\ = 13 \times 15 \quad = 195\,\text{cm}^2$
Area of back $= 5 \times 15 \quad\ = 75\,\text{cm}^2$
Total surface area $\qquad\quad = 510\,\text{cm}^2$

For a cylinder there are three surfaces.

The two ends each have area $= \pi r^2$.

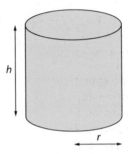

If the cylinder were made out of paper, the curved surface would open out to a rectangle.

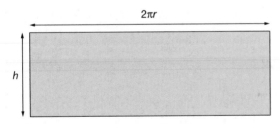

The length of the rectangle = the circumference of the cylinder = $2\pi r$.

The curved surface area is therefore $2\pi r \times h = 2\pi rh$.

Total surface area of a cylinder = $2\pi rh + 2\pi r^2$

EXAMPLE 5

Calculate the total surface area of a cylinder with base diameter 15 cm and height 10 cm.

Radius of base = 15 ÷ 2 = 7·5 cm

Area of two ends = $2 \times \pi r^2 = 2 \times \pi \times 7\cdot5^2 = 353\cdot4\,cm^2$

Curved surface area = $2\pi rh = 2 \times \pi \times 7\cdot5 \times 10 = 471\cdot2\,cm^2$

Total surface area = $353\cdot4 + 471\cdot2 = 825\,cm^2$, to the nearest whole number.

> **EXAM TIP**
>
> Before calculating the surface area of a prism, it may be useful to make a rough sketch of the net of the prism. This should stop you missing out a face.

EXERCISE 26.2

1 Find the total surface area of each of these shapes from Exercise 26.1.
  a) The cylinder in question **1**
  b) The cylinder in question **2**
  c) The cylinder in question **3**
  d) The prism in question **4a)**
  e) The cylinder in question **6**
  f) The cylinder in question **7**
  g) The cylinder in question **8**
  h) The prism in question **9a)**

2 Find the total surface area of each of these prisms.
  (You may wish to sketch the net of the prism first.)
  a)

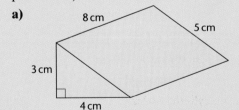

  b)

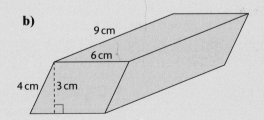

3 Find the total surface area of each of these shapes from Exercise 26.1.
  (You will need your answers to Exercise 26.1.)
  a) The cylinder in question **13**
  b) The cylinder in question **14**
  c) The cylinder in question **15**
  d) The cylinder in question **18**
  e) The cylinder in question **19**
  f) The cylinder in question **20**

STAGE

7

CHALLENGE 1

A prism has a cross-section which is an equilateral triangle with sides of 6 cm.
The length of the prism is 10 cm.

Find the total surface area of the prism.

Hint: You will need to use Pythagoras' theorem to find the height of the triangle.

 CHALLENGE 2

A prism has a cross-section which is an isosceles triangle with sloping sides of 10 cm and base 16 cm.

The length of the prism is 4·5 cm.

Find the total surface area of the prism.

Converting between measures

You already know the basic relationships between **linear** metric measures. 'Linear' means 'to do with length'.

You can use these relationships to work out the relationships between metric units of area and volume.

For example:

$1\,cm = 10\,mm$	$1\,m = 100\,cm$
$1\,cm^2 = 1\,cm \times 1\,cm$ $\quad\ = 10\,mm \times 10\,mm$ $\quad\ = 100\,mm^2$	$1\,m^2 = 1\,m \times 1\,m$ $\quad\ = 100\,cm \times 100\,cm$ $\quad\ = 10\,000\,cm^2$
$1\,cm^3 = 1\,cm \times 1\,cm \times 1\,cm$ $\quad\ = 10\,mm \times 10\,mm \times 10\,mm$ $\quad\ = 1000\,mm^3$	$1\,m^3 = 1\,m \times 1\,m \times 1\,m$ $\quad\ = 100\,cm \times 100\,cm \times 100\,cm$ $\quad\ = 1\,000\,000\,cm^3$

STAGE

7

EXAM TIP
1 litre = 1000 cm^3

EXAMPLE 6

Change these units.
a) $5\,m^3$ to cm^3 **b)** $5600\,cm^2$ to m^2

a) $5\,m^3 = 5 \times 1\,000\,000\,cm^3$ Convert $1\,m^3$ to cm^3 and multiply by 5.
$\qquad = 5\,000\,000\ cm^3$

b) $5600\,cm^2 = 5600 \div 10\,000\,m^2$ To convert from m^2 to cm^2 you multiply, so
$\qquad\quad = 0.56\ m^2$ to convert from cm^2 to m^2 you divide.

Make sure you have done the right thing by checking that your answer makes sense. If
you had multiplied by $10\,000$, you would have got $56\,000\,000\,m^2$, which is obviously a
much larger area than $5600\,cm^2$.

EXERCISE 26.3

Change the units in questions **1** to **5**.

1 **a)** 25 m to cm
   b) 42 cm to mm
   c) 2·36 m to cm
   d) 5·1 m to mm

2 **a)** $3\,m^2$ to cm^2
   b) $2\cdot3\,cm^2$ to mm^2
   c) $9\cdot52\,m^2$ to cm^2
   d) $0\cdot014\,cm^2$ to mm^2

3 **a)** $90\,000\,mm^2$ to cm^2
   b) $8140\,mm^2$ to cm^2
   c) $7\,200\,000\,cm^2$ to m^2
   d) $94\,000\,cm^2$ to m^2

4 **a)** $3\cdot2\,m^3$ to cm^3
   b) $42\,cm^3$ to m^3
   c) $5000\,cm^3$ to m^3
   d) $6\cdot42\,m^3$ to cm^3

5 **a)** 2·61 litres to cm^3
   b) 9500 ml to litres
   c) 2·4 litres to ml
   d) 910 ml to litres

6 What is wrong with this statement?
   'The trench I have just dug is 5 m long,
   2 m wide and 50 cm deep.
   To fill it in, I would need $500\,m^3$ of
   concrete.'

7 This carton holds 1 litre.
   How high is it?

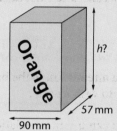

8 How many litres are there in 1 cubic
metre?

9 The cross-section of this piece of
guttering is a trapezium.
The length of the guttering is 2·4 m.
How many litres can it hold?

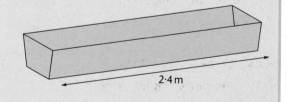

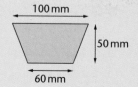

STAGE
7

EXERCISE 26.3 continued

10 This barrel is a cylinder and it holds 500 litres. It is 1·5 m high. Work out its diameter.

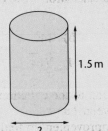

1.5 m

?

11 1 hectare = 10 000 m². How many hectares are there in 1 km²?

12 A sugar cube has sides of 15 mm. Find how many will fit in a box measuring 11 cm by 11 cm by 5 cm.

C CHALLENGE 3

Cleopatra is reputed to have had a bath filled with asses' milk.

Today her bath might be filled with cola!

Assuming that a can of drink holds 330 millilitres, approximately how many cans would she need to have a bath in cola?

K KEY IDEAS

■ Volume of a prism = area of cross-section × length

■ The total surface area of a solid is the total area of all the faces.

■ $1\,m^2 = 10\,000\,cm^2 = 1\,000\,000\,mm^2$

■ 1 litre = $1000\,cm^3$

■ $1\,m^3 = 1\,000\,000\,cm^3 = 1000$ litres

Revision exercise E1

1   The dimensions of a picture frame are given as 17 cm and 28 cm.
    Assuming that these are given to the nearest centimetre, what is the smallest each of these dimensions could be?

2   A boy gives his mass as 52·3 kg to 1 decimal place.
    Give the upper and lower bounds for this mass.

3   A mug holds 23·4 cl of liquid, correct to the nearest ml.
    What are the upper and lower bounds of the capacity of the mug?

4   The winning time in the school 200 m race was 27·94 seconds, correct to the nearest hundredth of a second.
    What are the upper and lower bounds of this time?

5   John is 1·75 m tall, correct to the nearest centimetre.
    What are the upper and lower bounds of his height?

6   A length is given as between 6·805 cm and 6·815 cm.
    a) What measurement would be recorded?
    b) What is its degree of accuracy?

7   Write these in a simpler form, using indices.
    a) $7^2 \times 7^3$ **b)** $6^3 \times 6^6$
    c) $10^9 \times 10^3$ **d)** $3^4 \times 3^8$
    e) $8^9 \div 8^3$ **f)** $6^9 \div 6^7$
    g) $4^3 \div 4^2$ **h)** $9^6 \div 9^2$
    i) $\dfrac{3^7 \times 3^3}{3^4}$

8   Simplify these.
    a) $x^2 \times x^4$ **b)** $x^5 \div x^2$
    c) $3a^3 \times 4a^2$ **d)** $6y^5 \div 2y^2$

9   Without using a calculator, write down these.
    a) $\sqrt{121}$ **b)** 14^2
    c) $\sqrt{169}$ **d)** $\sqrt[3]{64}$

10 There is a solution to the equation $x^3 - 7x = 0$ between 2 and 3.
    Use trial and improvement to find the solution correct to 1 decimal place.

11 Show that there is a solution to the equation $x^3 - 2x = 5$ between 2 and 3.
    Use trial and improvement to find the solution correct to 1 decimal place.

12 There is a solution to the equation $x^3 + 40 = 0$ between ⁻4 and ⁻3.
    Use trial and improvement to find the solution correct to 1 decimal place.

13 Each of these is the formula for the nth term of a sequence.
    Find the first four terms of each sequence.
    a) $n + 4$ **b)** $2n + 3$
    c) $3n - 2$ **d)** $8n$
    e) $15 - 2n$

14 Find the formula for the nth term of each of these sequences.
    a) 3   5   7   9
    b) 5   10   15   20
    c) 11   12   13   14
    d) 5   8   11   14
    e) ⁻2   ⁻4   ⁻6   ⁻8
    f) 17   14   11   8

15 Multiply out these brackets and simplify your answers.
    a) $(x + 6)(x + 3)$
    b) $(x + 7)(x - 4)$
    c) $(a - 6)(a + 5)$
    d) $(b - 3)^2$
    e) $(x - 5)(x - 8)$
    f) $(p + 3)(p - 3)$
    g) $(a + 8)^2$
    h) $(x + 8)(x - 8)$

STAG
7

E1

16 A prism 25 cm long has this L shape as its cross-section.
Calculate the volume of the prism.

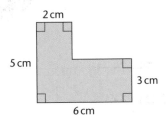

2 cm

5 cm

3 cm

6 cm

17 A cylindrical vase has internal radius 5·6 cm and height 22·5 cm.
Calculate how many litres of water the vase can hold.

18 The diagram shows a full-size net for a triangular prism.
Use measurements from the drawing to calculate
a) the surface area of the prism.
b) the volume of the prism.

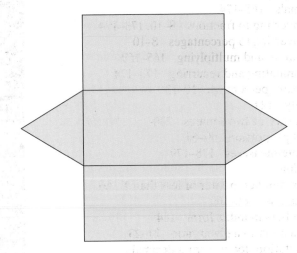

19 The diagram shows the cross-section of a prism which is 8 cm long.
Calculate
a) the height of the trapezium.
b) the volume of the prism.
c) the total surface area of the prism.

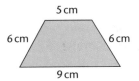

5 cm

6 cm   6 cm

9 cm

20 Change these units.
a) 2·45 m to cm
b) 4380 cm to m
c) 8·5 m² to cm²
d) 675 cm² to m²
e) 1·25 m³ to cm³
f) 750 000 cm³ to m³

TAGE
7

Index

STAGE

7

STAGE
7